The Most Vulnerable

Women, HIV, and Islam in Mali

by

Christopher A. Brooks

with translations by

Salim Coumare

LINUS
Learning

Published by Linus Learning

Ronkonkoma, NY 11779

ISBN 10: 1-60797-709-5

ISBN 13: 978-1-60797-709-4

Printed in the United States of America.

This book is printed on acid-free paper.

Print Number   5   4   3   2   1

Table of Contents

Chapter 1

Feeling of Contamination

Chapter 2

Learning from HIV

Chapter 3

Vulnerability through Denial

Chapter 4

Surviving Shame

Chapter 5

Educated and Infected

Chapter 6

Stigma in a Small Village

Chapter 7

Alone, but not Abandoned

Chapter 8

Marital Sacrifice

Chapter 29

Exiled by Stigma

Foreword

The Most Vulnerable: Women, HIV, and Islam in Mali is a timely book which explores several issues about the often precarious nature of women's experience in that West African country. This book grew out of interdisciplinary faculty affiliations with the Virginia Commonwealth University Institute for Women's Health and faculty community engagement activities through the Richmond Sister Cities Commission that was promoting women's health in Ségou, Mali. Researchers from the VCU medical and its Monroe Park campuses benefitted from grants awarded to institution by the Bill and Melinda Gates Foundation and the U.S. Department of Education.

Dr. Brooks' work with HIV-positive women uniquely contributes both to the existing body of scholarship and provides answers and understanding to questions being raised today by nonprofits, governmental agencies, and civil society. Unlike traditional theoretical and statistical-driven research, this book presents individual and collective documentation (from primary sources) covering a range of issues involving female health from a cultural, medical, and socio-economic perspective. Religion, mostly Islam in this case, is an important part of all three. In the book's introduction, Brooks posed a question – Why Mali?

In February 2012 the Richmond Sister Cities Commission inaugurated a maternity clinic in Ségou, Mali that had been built with Bill and Melinda Gates Foundation funding. The medical and political contacts established at the local, regional, and national levels in Mali during this undertaking were all in place when VCU applied for additional Gates funding to do a clinical study in Ségou in May 2012.

Brooks also asked - Why women? In March 2012, I called together a group of researchers in the VCU Institute for Women's Health to see if there should be a follow-up to the Sister Cities Commission work with a maternity center in Ségou. The head of the VCU HIV/AIDS Center responded favorably and proposed to develop his existing work on probiotics to include its preventive uses in HIV-positive women. His idea was to see if taking probiotics capsules would keep the disease from progressing into full-blown AIDS. The women considered for the probiotic study had not progressed to the stage where they needed to be placed on anti-retroviral treatments. However, had their health status warranted it, they would have been placed on an ART regimen. Faculty from VCU Nursing, Internal Medicine, Psychiatry, Anthropology, and French were all invited to participate in the interdisciplinary team.

The three anthropologists and the French faculty member related our research to international concerns about women's health and the role of women in African societies. While language and cultural issues were addressed most often by the three of us who are bilingual in French, all of us were interested in health care and society. The VCU Institute for Women's Health was in our opinion the logical home for the Gates grant.

Through the narratives in *The Most Vulnerable*, Brooks explores many issues related to cultural taboos, medical concerns of women who have little control over their sexuality, and societal reactions toward women and men with HIV. These are among the issues which inform Malian society's views on respect for women and support for their empowerment. The focus on Islam is particularly important because it is at a time when Muslim leaders in Africa and elsewhere are working across religions with nonprofits and government entities to help women and children address health issues in order to get the attention they deserve.

Another contributing factor to the invaluable quality of *The Most Vulnerable* was a gathering of scholars that took place at VCU in 2013 - the "Women, War and Peace in Africa Conference." Robin Poulton (whose own research interests includes issues of war and violence in Mali), and I co-chaired the conference which brought together scholars from the US and Africa. Dr. Poulton has also considered the impact of these conditions on the lives of women. As a seasoned grant writer and development administrator, Poulton's wife, Michelle, received the original Gates grant that would precipitate a series of developments which resulted in this very work. Her contacts among the medical community throughout Mali proved to be pivotal.

Through the work of foundations such as the Fondation Djigui la Grande Espérance, African Islam is paying greater attention to many women's health issues that have been overlooked in the past. Views such as women with HIV is an important concern for this and other foundations, and it is a topic receiving much discussion as clergy of all major religions now work together to promote respect for and empowerment of women. Women with HIV are prominently addressed.

My own work on the proceedings of our grant-funded Women, War, and Peace in Africa conference has led to discussions of women's health from varied perspectives and Christopher Brooks' remarkable work will be cited as we look at the role of women in war and peace. His research methodology is a courageous risk-taking search for truth through the poignant experiences of African women (and men) discussed in this book. Without doubt, it is an important contribution to the work of our research teams.

Patricia W. Cummins (PhD.),
Chair of the Richmond Sister Cities Commission,
Co-Principal Investigator of the VCU Gates HIV Project and
Principal Investigator of the VCU French West Africa Project

Acknowledgements

One of the most gratifying activities after completing a book manuscript is acknowledging those whose help and assistance had been invaluable to the successful completion of the work. As with my two previous HIV-related books, I want to acknowledge those individuals and agencies (in the case of this book, Mali) who welcomed me and the other research team members which made this work possible. Among them is the Malian Ministry of Health in Bamako. In Ségou there were several individuals and agencies that assisted me with this work including Abdoulaye Sanogo, Director General of the Nianankoro Hospital Fomba of Ségou. He identified several participants whose narratives are included in *The Most Vulnerable*. Dr. Sanogo also referred me to several clinics in Bamako and elsewhere, but by agreement and for confidentiality purposes, I have not included the names of those facilities.

I am forever grateful to my colleague and friend, Mahamadou Drabo, Director of the Walé Clinic also in Ségou. The work of that facility has literally transformed lives of many women and men who have sought counsel and treatment there. It was a pleasure for me to work at Walé with Dr. Drabo and his wonderful staff. I owe him much. I also thank Fanta Diabate of Bamako. She served as the in-country medical director of the Gates project. She also assisted me in locating women for this work and advised me on the many cultural practices that I should be prepared for.

There were several local government officials whose efforts were also integral to this work. That list includes the Honorable Boubacar Thierno Cissé, Governor of the Ségou region; the Honorable Ousmane K. Simaga, the Mayor of Ségou, and the Honorable Madani Sissoko, City Councilman and Chair of the Ségou Sister Cities Commission in Mali. I also gratefully wish to acknowledge the assistance of the Honorable Abdoul Gali Monsour Haidara, Deputy and President of the Cheick Mansour Haidara Foundation in Ségou.

I also wish to thank others based in Bamako including Professor Macki Samaké, Vice-Chancellor of the University of Arts and Social Sciences of Bamako; Professor Kalifa Touré, CEO of Cry of the Heart of Northern Mali and the University of Social Sciences and Management Bamako, and Yah Traoré. Your willingness to assist in this process will be remembered. There was an important women's group which I met, Keneyaton, also based in Ségou. These incredible women will surely lead the way to enlightening Mali to the correct path in addressing the HIV situation and many other social issues facing women of the country.

My initial trip to Mali in January 2013 was funded by the U.S. Department of Education's Title VI program called the Undergraduate International Studies and Foreign Languages Grant. That support was received by my colleague and dear friend, Patricia Cummins. She took a group of professors from Virginia Commonwealth University (VCU) including Helen Ruth Aspass, Brahima Koné,

Shawn Utsey, and Bernard Moitt. That trip was very ably and professionally shepherded by Robin and Michelle E. Poulton of the Epes Mandela Corporation. At about the same time that Title VI grant was received, Dr. Cummins was notified that she had also received a Bill and Melinda Gates Foundation Grand Explorations in Health grant to support research among HIV positive Women in Mali. Cummins served as the co-investigator of the Gates grant with Daniel Nixon, Director of the VCU HIV/ AIDS Center. Also a part of this worthy endeavor was the VCU Women's Health Institute directed by Susan Kornstein. Others who were a part of that research team included Saba Masho (also of the Women's Institute), and Nancy Jallo of the VCU School of Nursing. I am grateful to all of these professionals for welcoming me to the group. I also wish to thank Ana Edwards, President of the Virginia Friends of Mali and her predecessor, Allan Levenburg.

I also want to acknowledge my colleagues in the VCU Anthropology Program including Noel Boaz, Christopher Stevenson, Amy Rector Verrelli, Matthew Pawlowicz, Edward Abse, Bernard Means, and Richard Harrington. There were also my other VCU colleagues, Kathryn Murphy-Judy and Eugenia Muñoz who always offer a kind word and much assistance. I am also grateful to the Humanities and Sciences' deans' office.

My students have played an important role in all of my books. I was fortunate to have had two student interns who assisted me at various stages of this book. I am grateful to Gonzalo Campero and Charlotte Russell both of whom were outstanding student assistants. In spring 2016, I taught my graduate course, *HIV in Africa* and the students in that class assisted me by reading through and commenting on an early draft of the manuscript. I am grateful to acknowledge Judith Bandoh, Caroline Butler, Kenza Faik, Viodia Jallah, Kendra Jones, Nicholas Mann, Darnell Reed, Charlotte Russell (also mentioned above), Marrissa Spence, Tyriq Taliferro, Carlina Tavarez, and Sean Treasure for their willingness to offer their comments and holding me to a high standard. Martin Townes, also my student, assisted me with the bibliography, and reading the manuscript.

I also want to thank my dear friends in Mali. Inah Niare, who provided much needed context for several situations that I encountered in the country and Salim Coumare, who acted as my coach, translator, and assistant in the second phase of my field work in Mali. Salim was able to come to the US to participate in a public lecture while he and I worked through the translations of *The Most Vulnerable*. When writing books, I always rely of the editorial assistance of my brother-in-law, Thomas J. Brown, and my good friend, Bob Daniels who has helped with several of my literary projects. I am thankful to have them both nearby.

There is a hard to define category of assistance when completing a book which I hate to call miscellaneous because without the support from those people, this work might not have been successfully completed. I am pleased to thank my friends Charles J. Hackett, Jr., and Morris G. Henderson as well as my children in Kenya, David and Rahab Kimani. As before, I thank my sister Cheryle Brooks Johnson, and my brother Lowry M. Brooks, both of whom knew my whereabouts. I dutifully thank St. Paul's Catholic Church for providing me with a quiet place to work.

Lastly, I thank the women and men who heroically shared their HIV narratives with me. They deserve foremost recognition and my deepest appreciation. It was not an easy task for many of the women whose stories are presented here. Many have justifiably feared persecution or some form of ostracization were they to disclose their HIV status. That said, I am grateful that you trusted me with the responsibility of telling your stories. I hope you won't be disappointed. Again, I thank you all for your unwavering support.

Christopher Brooks

Introduction

The Most Vulnerable: Women, HIV, and Islam in Mali is the third of my HIV-related books and is an outgrowth of my second such work, *Through the Voices of Men: South African Men Speak about HIV* (Linus Books 2011 first edition and 2013 second edition), which examined the virus from the viewpoint of South African men. While researching that book, I met with several Muslim men who expressed the collective feeling that the religion was not as tolerant of those with the virus as they had hoped. As a result, according to them, there was considerable stigma, and an atmosphere of shame was cast on them. And there was the general belief that one who contracted the virus was somehow morally questionable and had not properly adhered to the tenets of the religion.

With that working assumption, *The Most Vulnerable* presents the narratives of twenty six women (twenty three of whom are Muslim) who give an account of their HIV experience in that West African country. Since the modern-day appearance of the virus in the early 1980s, women and children have been affected in far greater numbers by HIV than men. Without question, the stigma surrounding this virus has fallen disproportionately on women.[1] My justification for focusing on men and the virus in two prior books was that they were more likely to infect their female partners than the other way around. Women and children rightfully should have been at the center of HIV/AIDS research because it is well known that the most vulnerable person to this virus world-wide is still a married woman. *The Most Vulnerable,* sadly, reinforces that reality.

WOMEN, ISLAM AND THE HIV VIRUS

Why the focus on women and Mali? Through the generosity of the Bill and Melinda Gates Foundation's Grand Challenges Explorations in Health, I was invited to be a part of an international team of researchers whose research focus was in monitoring activity in the guts (which is a more reliable repositor of the HIV antigens than the blood) of seropositive women in Mali. By introducing a probiotic to the various participants in the study, it is hoped that strengthening these women's digestive systems would boost their ability to resist the debilitating impact of the virus. In addition to the Gates grant, I was part of another research team which was funded by the Department of Education's Title VI program. These research collaborations were with the Virginia Commonwealth University HIV/AIDS Center, the College of Humanities and Sciences, the VCU Women's Health Institute, and several Malian universities and partner agencies including the Malian Ministry of Health.

These projects presented me with the opportunity to explore issues that have been a priority for me for close to two decades. I have been working on the African

---

1   See Raqiz, Mohamed Y, "The HIV/AIDS Epidemic in Muslim Africa: Tanzania as a Case Study."

continent for more than thirty years, but this is the first time that I have worked in an exclusively Francophone setting. I also saw this as an occasion to work among a predominantly Muslim population (Mali is 90% Muslim). And there was the opportunity (and challenge) to work with women and to hear firsthand how the virus had altered their lives.

This work presented other challenges. There is no single Islamic practice for the approximately 1.6 billion followers of the faith worldwide. Many specialist and non-specialist are aware of separation between Sunni and Shi'ite (also known as Shia) sects within the Muslim faith. Some of those differences are pronounced, depending on the geographical location. The fundamental split came about when no clear successor was identified by the prophet Muhammad before his death. As none of his sons lived to be adults, a familial line of succession could not occur. Those who came to identify themselves as Shi'ites believe the prophet's cousin and son-in-law, Ali, should have been his rightful successor. Those followers of Sunni Islam believed his father-in-law and close friend, Abu Bakr, should be his successor. Of that one billion and a half Muslims today, about 85% are Sunnis and the balance are Shi'ites or some other sect of Islam.[2] These various Islamic practices have been modified significantly throughout Africa as indigenous cultural dynamics have necessarily played a role in their adaptation.[3] There are also differences based on Qur'anic scriptural interpretation as well as other religious works. The majority of Malian Muslims identify as Sunnis.

As the renowned Islamic feminist scholar (and my former colleague), Amina Wadud, has written about for years, women and men should be treated equally according to the teachings of the Qur'an.[4] She maintains that passages in the *Qur'an* as well as those in the *Hadith* (the work containing lessons and teachings left by the Prophet Muhammad) have routinely been misinterpreted to the disadvantage of women throughout the history of the religion. Additionally, Wadud maintains, there should be no pronounced distinctions between men and women's inherent

---

2   http://www.pewresearch.org/fact-tank/2016/07/22/muslims-and-islam-key-findings-in-the-u-s-and-around-the-world/. Major countries in the Middle East, however, have large Shia populations. For example Iran has a 90% Shia population and Iraq has about a 50% Shia population.

3   Sana Loue commented in "AIDS Jihad: Integrating the Islamic Concept of Jihad with HIV Prevention Theory," "Temporary marriage, permitted among Shi'ite Muslims but forbidden among Sunni Muslims, may lead to increased HIV risk. This form of marriage allows individuals to engage in sexual intercourse with serial sexual partners without religious or social disapproval. Al Jazeera television reported in 2003 an increase in so-called summer marriages or travel marriages in the Gulf States. These marriages, occurring between young girls from lower-income families and visiting Arab tourists, are entered into in exchange for a bride price to be paid to the girl's family. The marriages are often terminated through divorce at the end of the husband's vacation in the area."

4   See Wadud, Amina. *The Qur'an and Woman: Rereading the Sacred Text from a Woman's Perspective*. New York: Oxford University Press, 1999. Also see Wadud, Amina. *The Gender Jihad: Women's Reform in Islam.* Oxford: One World Press, 2006.

roles and positions where the faith is concerned. However, that has often not been the case in most Muslim-majority countries.

Within that context, the Malian story is revealing. In the March 2016 *Enquête par grappes à Indicateurs Multiples (MICS) 2015 Rapport* (Indicators Cluster Survey Multiples (MICS) 2015 Results report) issued by the Malian Ministère de L'Aménagement du Territoire et de la Population (Department of Land and Population), gender issues and attitudes are quite striking. In the area of gender-based violence, for instance, the report questioned men and women between the age of fifteen and forty-nine who believed it was permissible for a man to strike or beat his wife under the following circumstances: (1) she goes out without telling him; (2) she neglects the children; (3) she openly disagrees with him; (4) she refuses to have sex with him, and (5) she burns the food. The percentage of Malian men agreeing with physical punishment of their wives under these conditions was 50.9 percent. But the percentage of women agreeing that beatings were the appropriate response to such activities by a husband was a startling 72.6 percent.[5]

The submission of Muslim women in Africa (including Mali) to their husbands and male partners is often routine and the narratives in *The Most Vulnerable* bare this reality out. Women who attempt to rebel or speak out are often suppressed, or face some other form of social ostracization. They could even be subjected to, as the above mentioned statistics indicate, physical violence. It is also well known that many continental African women do not have the ability to negotiate condom usage with their husbands or male partners. The *Voices of Men* made clear the importance that many African societies place on childbearing, which means that rite of passage (i.e. mothering or fathering children) is often placed above contracting HIV.[6] Mali has been no exception and a majority of women in *The Most Vulnerable* are, in fact, mothers or have that status as an ambition.

SPREAD OF HIV IN MUSLIM DOMINATED COUNTRIES AND MALI

Two decades ago (i.e. the mid-1990s), most Muslim-dominated countries boasted of their comparatively low HIV rates and attributed those numbers to the strict adherence to the tenets of Islam which discourages alcohol consumption, premarital and extra marital sex, and drug use. The more likely explanation for the low prevalence rate was the Muslim practice of medical male circumcision which can reduce the rate of HIV infection by as much as 60% in an unprotected

---

5 *Enquête par grappes à Indicateurs Multiples (MICS) 2015 Rapport de Résultats Clés*, March 2016, p. 16. Part of this number must take into account that many rural women are likely to agree with such a position as opposed to urban women.

6 See Brooks, *Voices of Men*. See the narrative of Elias Mamabolo among other narratives. Also see the *Enquête par grappes à Indicateurs Multiples (MICS) 2015 Rapport de Résultats Clés* which stated that only 17.2 per cent of women (between 15-49) reported using a condom during a sexual encounter as compared to 31.0 per cent of men in the same age category.

sexual encounter.[7] Many Muslim-dominated countries also underreported their HIV statistics.

Over the last decade (i.e. 2000 - 2010), however, there has been an across-the-board increase in HIV infections in most Muslim-dominated countries in the Middle East and North Africa.[8] Certain West African countries like Chad and Nigeria reported HIV prevalence rates of more than 3.0% (Chad 3.4% and Nigeria 3.6% respectively).[9] Some Muslim-dominated countries in West Africa, have, however lowered their collective HIV prevalence rate including Senegal, because they have actively engaged men and women in the mosques about the impact of HIV as well as maintained comprehensive screening of marginalized groups at high risk.[10]

With regard to Mali, the most frequent diseases continue to be malaria, respiratory infections, and diarrhea.[11] The country's overall seropositive rate is 1.7% with a slightly higher percentage (2.0%) in the Ségou region.[12] According to the regional *Plan de Lutte Contre Le VIH/SIDA en Zone Office du Niger* (Plan to Fight against HIV/AIDS in the Niger Area), women between the ages of twenty-five and thirty-four, the seropositive rate is 2.3%. For women between twenty-five and twenty-nine, the seropositive rate was 3.4% and for street vendors (women and men) the seropositive rate was 6.8%.[13] Other major urbans areas such as Bamako, Sikasso, and Kayes report similar seropositive rates, if not higher.

There are other contributing factors which facilitate the spread of the virus in Mali which include young girls who migrate from rural areas to urban areas such as Bamako, Ségou, Sikasso, and Kayes to work as domestics and often get drawn into sexual enslavement because of their naiveté. Sometimes these girls resort to sex work out of economic necessity. Yet another scenario occurs when young ladies migrate to Ivory Coast or Burkina Faso to raise money for their pending marriages and are similarly drawn into some sexual scenario which results in

---

7   See Brooks, *Voices of Men*.

8   See Yamaguchi, Kaoru, "HIV/AIDS in the Muslim-Majority Countries: Formula for Low Prevalence." Also see UNAIDS *2010 Global Report* (2010).

9   WHO *Global HIV/AIDS responses: Epidemic update and health sector progress towards Universal Access. Progress report 2011*.

10   Benton, Adia. *HIV Exceptionalism: Development through Disease in Sierra Leone*. Minneapolis: University of Minnesota Press, 2015. Also see Yamaguchi Kaoru. *HIV/AIDS in the Muslim-Majority Countries: Formula for Low Prevalence*. 2012.

11   Office du Niger Ségou. *Plan de Lutte Contre Le VIH/SIDA en Zone Office du Niger*. No date

12   *Plan de Lutte Contre Le VIH/SIDA en Zone Office du Niger*. Some sources place this rate at 1.4%.

13   *Plan de Lutte Contre Le VIH/SIDA*.

their infection. The migration scenario can also occur with young men who might also have traveled southwards to Ivory Coast or Burkina Faso for employment as seasonal workers.

As the third major exporter of gold in Africa, Mali's so-called "Gold trail" has lured men, women and children from surrounding areas, the region and other parts of the continent to work in the mines and rivers where gold is harvested.[14] Even though gold mining is a multimillion dollar business, the wages are remarkably low and can draw young girls and boys into situations which make them vulnerable to contracting the virus.

RELIGION OR CULTURE

At the heart of this work is the dynamic between the Islamic faith and the role that Malian culture plays in the spread of the virus. Specifically, while the majority of Malians are Muslims (a religion that has taken a somewhat detached approach to HIV), will they defer to their culture when faced with a health crisis such as HIV? In *Through the Voices of Men*, my working hypothesis was grappling with the issue of African masculinity and the role that it played in the contraction and spread of the virus. As noted in several narratives in that work, the Zulu concept of *isoka* (the manifestation of male sexual prowess based on the number of females a male engages with sexually) became the theoretical foundation of that book.[15] *The Most Vulnerable* relies on several works to frame this discussion about faith vis-à-vis culture. Noemi Steuer's article, "We are afraid of what others may say about us: Maintaining honor and respect in processes of disclosure in Bamako, Mali," in *Medische Anthropologie* set the initial tone for this work in establishing the importance of keeping one's seropositive status secret. Because of the social implications including the importance of maintaining one's good name, a clear cultural indicator, there were certain drawbacks to revealing one's seropositivity. Steuer stated, "Although the biological aspects of the disease can be controlled with antiretroviral therapy, the gossip of those around her [i.e. a woman with a seropositive diagnosis] might jeopardize her social existence."[16] This statement supports the position of practically every woman in *The Most Vulnerable*. All of them have been given a pseudonym to protect their identity and those of their families. Even though all informants were videotaped from the neck down, one of the women, Fatima Musa (a pseudonym), was fearful enough that her identity

---

14   Kippenberg, Julianne. *"Dispatches: Gold Refiners Should Act on Child Labor"* Human Rights Watch June 12, 2015.

15   This concept of male sexual prowess is articulated in the article by Ingrid Lynch, et. al., "Constructed of masculinity among a group of South African men living with HIV/AID: reflections on resistance and change." *Culture, Health & Sexuality* Vol. 12, No. 1 January 2010: 15 – 27.

16   Steuer, Noemi. "'We are just afraid of what others may say about us.' Maintaining honor and respect in processes of disclosure in Bamako, Mali." *Medische Anthropologie* 24 (2) 2012: 266 – 287.

would be compromised, believing that someone might recognize her by the clothes she was wearing. I had to spend time assuring her that only I and a few of my trusted colleagues would have confidential access to the recorded interviews. This was indicative of the level of the fear of persecution that many of these women were rightfully afraid of. Women (and men) fear being referred to pejoratively as a "sidéen" or "sidéenne" (a man or woman with AIDS referred to as "SIDA" in French).

As a result of my work in South Africa, I became an advocate of that country's campaign to remove the stigma of HIV by encouraging seropositive persons to reveal their statuses. Such a revelation, by that reasoning, would weaken the social stranglehold of the virus. I was persuaded that there was merit in this approach worldwide to combat the negative perceptions of HIV. I quickly found that such was not the case in Mali. It was only after guaranteeing their total anonymity, did several of the women agree to proceed.

Steuer also pointed out that from the modern emergence of the HIV epidemic in the 1980s, a seropositive woman was often linked somehow to commercial sex work and therefore the virus was identified as a *maladie honteuse* (a shameful disease).[17] Although Steuer pointed to the national statute of 2006 that requires those with knowledge of their HIV positive status in the country to report this information to their sexual partners within six weeks of their diagnosis, very few of the husbands or male partners of the women in *The Most Vulnerable* followed this directive. Many of the men not only kept their seropositive status silent, but in several cases accused the wife or female partner of giving *them* the virus.[18] In fact, not a single woman in the book (whether educated or preliterate) raised the issue of the 2006 statute which suggests that it is not well known, much less being enforced. The accumulative effect of these realities in Mali has resulted in an all too familiar atmosphere of shame that has been reported in my previous writings on the subject.

There is certainly a connection between social standing and a woman's ability to withstand the stigma that often comes with disclosing one's serostatus. Ami Cissé, Mariatou Dembele, and Mary Thera are among the women in *The Most Vulnerable* who had adequate economic resources or a strong family foundation to shield them from the social isolation that several other women have justifiably feared.

The second influential work framing aspects of this book is Kaoru Yamaguchi's *HIV/AIDS in the Muslim-Majority Countries: Formula for Low Prevalence*.[19] This comprehensive senior thesis from Bemidji State University in Minnesota draws on the Malian HIV experience as a case study, and makes several insightful

---

17   Steuer, Noemie p. 270.

18   Présidence de la République, *Recuil des textes sur la lute contre le VIH/sida*. Bamako : Haut Consiel National de Lutte Contre le Sida, 2006.

19   Yamaguchi Kaoru. *HIV/AIDS in the Muslim-Majority Countries: Formula for Low Prevalence*. 2012.

observations regarding stigma, preliteracy, illicit drug use, sexual behaviors, and the lack of female empowerment as contributing factors to the increase seropositive rates in the country.

From the start, Yamaguchi dispelled the myth of Muslim-majority countries having a low HIV/AIDS rate because of Islam's "strict religious and moral codes."[20] In fact, many of these countries had underreported their HIV statistics and failed to recognize the spread of the virus within their populations.[21]

He cited illicit drug use as a significant factor in seropositivity especially in several Middle Eastern and North African Muslim countries, including Iran with an HIV prevalence rate of 15%; Pakistan 10.8%; Oman 11.8%, and Libya with an astounding 22%.[22]

Of the least spoken about aspects of HIV contraction and spread in Muslim-dominated countries in the Middle East and Africa is the reality of male same sex engagements which includes male sex workers and men who have sex with men (MSM). Yamaguchi (2012) and Niang (2003) are among others who have examined this underexplored topic. Because MSM activity is strictly looked down upon in Islam, there are few who are willing to admit to such engagements and are less willing to come forward to seek treatment. To compound the severity of this situation, a near majority of African states have laws on the books which outlaw MSM activities with the threat of imprisonment, floggings, and torture. Several countries (including several in Africa) have death penalty statutes on the books for MSM conduct.[23] Although Mali is not among those countries that formally bans same sex relationships, there is little support for any such engagements, which makes this population more vulnerable and less likely to come forward for testing and counseling. Were a man to admit to a MSM encounter, he is likely to be looked down upon and certainly not likely to receive a sympathetic voice for such behavior. While there was no direct evidence of such activity represented in *The Most Vulnerable*, it cannot be ruled out. These observations point to Malian culture's undeniable influence on the spread of the virus. It will be demonstrated below how this culture over religion dynamic continues to manifest itself.

DEMOGRAPHICS AND HIV IN WEST AFRICA

Mali is a large land locked country in West Africa with a population that exceeds fifteen million people. There are approximately fourteen ethnic groups including,

---

20   *HIV/AIDS in the Muslim-Majority Countries*, p. 4.

21   UNAIDS *2010 Global Report* (2010).

22   Yamaguchi citing Mathers et. al. (2008).

23   Interestingly, many continental African countries have banned MSM activity, but recognize same sex relationships between women to be legal.

Bambera, Bobo, Dogon, Fulani, Malinke, Minianka, Peul, Samogo, Sarakole, Senufo, Somono (also known as the Bozo), Soninke, and Tuareg. These are the ethnic groups represented in *The Most Vulnerable*. These women come from a variety of socio-cultural experiences as well as differing economic backgrounds. These narratives are striking for their honesty which reflects other realities of Malian society and nearby predominating Muslim states.

TRUCKING ROUTES

The Trans-African Highway trucking routes are found all over the continent and connect the east to the west and the north to the southern parts of Africa. West Africa has several major routes which have easy access to Mali. It was well established by the early 1990s that yet another contributing factor to the cross border spread of HIV among African countries was the trucking routes and those stops. Trucking stops (which likely include overnight stays) attract sex workers and with that came the spread of the virus.[24]

The highway "rest stops" attract sex workers, and hence there is a higher seropositivity rate along these routes. Ramjee et. al. (2002) documented this phenomenon in southern Africa more than a decade ago.

Similar activity has taken place along the West African trucking highways, especially those that have direct access or travel routes through Mali. The Malian capital, Bamako, is a major stop along the Dakar to Ndjamena route which includes stops in Kita, Kayes, Diéma, Didjeni, and Sikasso. Trucking Route 5 Dakar to Lagos also offers ample access to Mali. The cumulative effects have resulted in increased HIV rates among truckers along those routes who then spread the virus as they travel across country borders.

MILITARY

Another well documented phenomenon that has contributed to the HIV prevalence rate collectively within African countries is the higher than average infection rate among military personnel (especially soldiers) on the continent. The phenomenon is often attributed to the combination of two high risks groups. That is young men in their sexual prime (i.e. 15 – 25 years old) and the reality of women, who as a result of war or other conflicts on the continent, have been drawn into commercial sex work out of economic desparation.[25] While this combination is not unique to the African continent, the reality is very much present. This higher HIV rate in the military was documented in the early 1990s in the southern part

24   Bwayo J, Plummer F, Omari M, et. al. "Human immunodeficiency virus infection in long distance truck drivers in east Africa." *Archives of Internal Medicine*, June 27, 154 (12) 1994: 1391 – 1396.

25   Fleshman, Michael, "AIDS prevention in the ranks UN targets peacekeepers, combatants in war against the disease." *Africa Recovery*, June 2001.

ᴇ continent.[26] There was so much interest in the increased seropositive rate
ᴉg African militaries, the United Nations Security Council issued resolution
₁₃₀₀ in 2000 which raised concerns about the HIV rate increase in general, with
specific attention to Africa.[27] The resolution also called on its internal agency
UNAIDS to increase its involvement in stemming the seropositivity among this
particular sector by providing UN peacekeepers and other military personnel with
appropriate training and knowledge of HIV prevention.

The Malian military has unfortunately been consistent with the higher than
average seropositive rates on the African continent. There are several narratives in
The Most Vulnerable in which HIV positive women had husbands who are currently
serving or are former military men. Unlike the larger population, because of its
ability to effect certain changes by direct orders, the Malian military is in a position
to set the stage for HIV education and lead the way for the greater Malian society.[28]

OMNIPRESENT TRADITIONAL HEALERS

Another phenomenon which points to the significant role of culture over religion
in Mali (as well as other continental African countries) is the presence and reliance
on traditional healers. In the *Voices of Men* and elsewhere I have written about
the influence of traditional healers, and although Mali is a Muslim-dominated
country, the average woman (and man) is likely to consult a healer as part of their
medical diagnosis regimen. The advice offered by these healers was sometimes
counterproductive as in the case of Asiata Togola, and Fatimata Keita, where the
healer implicated them in some sorcery or accused them of some other kind of
malfeasance. However, the advice was productive in the cases of Rebecca Kansaye
and Djelika Kouyate where the respective traditional healer referred them to a
formal HIV testing clinic. Two of the men whose narratives are included, namely
Seydou Tangara, and Aliou Djire also consulted them.

In that traditional healers are consulted by Christians and Muslims across
all ethnicities in Mali, it seems that the country should follow the direction of
other West African countries like Ghana where a partnership between traditional
healers and western-trained medical personnel has been very fruitful and lacks an

---

26 See Greg Mills "AIDS and the South African Military: Timeworn Cliché or Time bomb?" *HIV/AIDS: a Threat to the African Renaissance?* Occasional paper (Johannesburg, South Africa: Konrad Adenauer Foundation, 2000. Also see Fleshman 2001.

27 UN Security Council Resolution 1308 on the Responsibility of the Security Council in the Maintenance of International Peace and Security: HIV/AIDS and International Peace-keeping Operations. July 2000.

28 Diallo S, Toloba Y, Coulibaly SA, Dabitao D, Diop S, Doumbia S, Keita B. "Male circumcision and HIV in the Malian military." Le *Mali Médical.* 23 (1) 2008: 45-6.

adversarial tone.[29] Mali might also want to consider forming a partnership with healers similar to the model used in South Africa.[30]

FORMAT AND SCOPE OF *THE MOST VULNERABLE*

Unlike my two previous HIV-related books, in which I was working with a mostly English-speaking population, Mali's lingua franca is French. Although I have basic facility with that language, I am far from fluent which required me to rely on several assistants, most notably Salim Coumare (who is fluent in both French and one of the country's other major indigenous languages, Bamanankan) for translation and interpreting purposes. I also used a questionnaire to obtain certain information, which was also a first for me.

Among the questions I asked were: Are you a Malian? To which ethnic group do you belong; what is your age? What is your religious affiliation? What is your family background? What is your marital status? Once those questions were answered, I inquired about their knowledge of the Human Immunodeficiency Virus with questions like: What is your knowledge of the virus? When did you first hear of it? What did you understand about the contraction and spread of the virus? What was your reaction to the news of your seropositive status? Who knows of your seropositive status? If your status is known, have you experienced any negative reaction from your family or community?

Based on my work in South Africa with the now defunct HIV support group called Positive Muslims, I was curious to know if such an organization (set up to assist seropositive Muslims) could be viable in Mali. So, I informed all of my Muslim participants in Mali that I had worked with such a group in South Africa. And I then asked if such an organization could work in Mali? Resoundingly, the answer was no. A few of my informants indicated that such an organization might work in the future, but was not a realistic possibility at this time. The majority of informants, however, rejected such a support group outright and said they would not participate in such a group were one to form. This was also the response from the Christians whom I interviewed. This is a troubling observation, because it suggests that stigma is still very prevalent and is preventing people (even those who have accepted their seropositive status and are in care) from assisting others who might benefit from the counsel of those who are managing the virus.

---

29   Warren, DM, and G S Bova, "Ghanaian national policy toward indigenous healers. The case of the primary health training for indigenous healers (PREHTIH) program," *Social Science Medicine*, 1982: 16 (21): 1873-81. *The Healers of Ghana* is a documentary which explores the traditional medical practices of the Bono people of central Ghana and how their healers are accommodating the conflict between the arrival of Western medicine and their religious beliefs.

30   The South African government has wisely included traditional healers in its nation-wide South African National AIDS Council (SANAC).

It was encouraging to see that many of the women have broken the cycle of silence about their status and informed their sons and daughters who were at or nearing adulthood. They have initiated such conversations with the goal of preventing their children from contracting the virus. This means they have had to discuss risky sexual behavior not only with their daughters, but also with their sons. Miriam Kouriba, Karitio Dembele, Sarah Coulibaly, Ami Cissé, and Sitan Kane are among those women who have had that conversation with their sons. In previous times, such discussions would never have taken place.

The narratives for *The Most Vulnerable* were collected in three field trips to Mali in 2013, 2014, and a follow up trip in 2015. Although I was based in Bamako and Ségou, interviews were collected in other geographical locations. I was requested not to disclose the balance of those locations because of confidentiality reasons (which was yet another manifestation of the secrecy that still pervades HIV in Mali). The meetings typically lasted two to three hours and each of the informants signed a consent agreement.

At the conclusion of the meeting, each informant received a stipend for their participation. There was a clause in the consent agreement allowing for each participant to withdraw their narrative if they decided to do so, despite the fact that all participants had been promised a pseudonym. Four women, whose narratives were collected, reconsidered their participation and asked (through a contact) that their interviews be withdrawn from this work. Those withdrawal requests were honored.

To bring some balance to the work, I also interviewed three men to further elucidate the overall experience. Those narratives appear as the last three chapters in the book. I could have very easily interviewed more men, but felt such an inclusion might diffuse the primary focus on women. So that number was limited to three.

CONCLUSION

While several of these narratives are painful, many also demonstrate the strength and perseverance of these women and their willingness to rigorously engage their seropositive status and combat it. They also make clear that there is much work to be done to successfully change the course and perception of this epidemic. While several of these women had economic resources and family support to cushion them from the social isolation that often accompanies an HIV diagnosis, the majority of women do not. There is also an issue of appropriate HIV education and the gender gap therein. The *Enquête par grappes à Indicateurs Multiples (MICS) 2015 Rapport de Résultats Clés* cited above offered clear indications of the challenges facing Mali. For example, when posed with the question of how to properly protect themselves from HIV transmission, only 19.1% of women between ages fifteen and twenty-four knew the correct way of blocking the transmission. More than thirty per cent (32.3 %) of men in the same age range knew the proper prevention methods.[31] The same report also indicated that more men (at 53.1%) knew where to go for HIV testing and counseling than women (at 35.7%). This conclusion may have something to do with men having greater knowledge of male condoms and where they may be able to obtain them.

Within the last year (i.e. 2015), Mali has experienced several high-profile terrorist attacks in the capital and other major urban areas. In the past, these jihadist actions had been concentrated in the northern part of the country. Given Mali's collective economic challenges, the political situation is not likely to be settled soon. These realities do not portend an especially promising educational advancement surrounding HIV/AIDS. Because of their "rigid" adherence to the tenets of Islam, there are sectors of the country where HIV testing and counseling is likely to lag or be nonexistent. Unfortunately, the areas which will be most affected will be rural areas and certain urban areas where the virus has continued to grow.

That said, there is much to be learned from the narratives in *The Most Vulnerable*. They demonstrate the challenges facing the women of Mali, and their efforts to deal with the Human Immunodeficiency Virus. It will take the joint involvement of local and state governments to recognize, address and handle this virus.

Christopher A. Brooks,
Professor of Anthropology
Virginia Commonwealth University

---

31   *Enquête par grappes à Indicateurs Multiples (MICS) 2015 Rapport* p. 18.

UN Security Council Resolution 1308 on the Responsibility of the Security Council in the Maintenance of International Peace and Security: HIV/AIDS and International Peace-keeping Operations. July 2000.

CHAPTER 1

Feeling of Contamination

Miriam Kouriba (pseudonym) is a preliterate Malian Muslim woman originally from Mopti. She is forty-six years old and is the youngest and only daughter among six siblings.

I had five older brothers. Two of them have passed away within the last ten years. I don't know if it was the virus or not. They simply got sick and deteriorated over a time. They both died. Based on what I now know, it very well may have been the virus. People in this country are very quiet about such things. Fortunately, my parents were already gone and did not have to endure the loss of their sons. I still have three brothers who are alive.

My parents were very poor. My father mostly farmed and my mother stayed at home to take care of things there. When I got a little older, I worked in the farm with my father and brothers. I also sold small items (mostly crafts) to help out the family. There was no money to send any of us to school, so I never learned to read or write.

When I was about seventeen, I was married. It was an arranged situation. As I was an only daughter, my father got a reasonable sum of money for me to wed. I was my husband's only wife - at least officially. When I left my father's home, not only was I a virgin, I knew practically nothing about sex. I only knew that after I got married I was supposed to submit to my husband's will. That meant being a good wife (and mother) and having sex when he wanted it. The first time I had sex with my husband it was very painful.

My husband was a good man, overall, and a good provider. He worked, pumping gas at a petrol station and later as a car repairman. I gave him six children – three boys and three girls. My oldest son is twenty five and the youngest child is eight. I lost one of my sons in an accident. It was so terrible, that I thought I would not live through that ordeal.

The first talk that I heard of HIV was on television and the radio in the late 2000s. It was in the same timeframe that my husband began having these routine illnesses. First, he would have the flu, and then a violent cough which would last for days. He also sweated at night a lot. I decided that I needed to take him to the hospital in Ségou for an examination. He resisted the very idea of going to see a doctor, because he thought it was unmanly. He kept saying, "It is in the hands of God." I had to contact his family and they helped me to persuade him to seek medical attention. He was disturbed with me about me going behind his back to his family, but I didn't have a choice. One of the doctors asked if he could give my husband an HIV test. I am not sure my husband understood exactly what was taking place, but he agreed and tested seropositive.

Just after we got the news of his seropositive results, the same doctor suggested that I also be tested. I just kept my eyes closed, because I knew enough about the virus at that point to know if someone had engaged in unprotected sexual relations, they were also at risk. I should not have been surprised to find out that I too was HIV positive. I was terrified! All I could think about was my children. Who would look after my children? I was not especially angry with my husband for some reason. He had told me he wanted to have another wife. I just thought he had slept with another woman who had given him the virus, which he in turn gave me.

I had a follow up appointment at the Ségou Hospital. When I went, I met other women who were also positive. These women who were supposed to be HIV positive didn't look sick like my husband. In fact many of them looked very healthy. When I raised this issue with a counselor, I was told that they took their medication as directed. I was told that if I followed my medication regimen I would be able to live to see my children grow up and be happy. My husband and I were told how the virus spread through sexual relationships, contaminated blood coming in contact with an open wound, and mother to child transmission.

Unlike me, however, my husband did not adhere to his medication regimen as he had been told. He sporadically took his meds. And at one point he totally stopped taking them all together. He had other health issues. The hospital psychologist was attempting to help him with some other problems which were not necessarily health related. Eventually, my husband's health deteriorated more and he died in 2011. After his death, I heard that three of his girlfriends had also died of the virus. I tried not to be too upset with him. I checked with one of his brothers about the death of these girlfriends and he said he didn't know anything about them.

I was encouraged to join the women's health initiative, Keneyaton. The women in that group have been very helpful to me. It fact, they have been a blessing. Not only do they provide support and counsel, but they mentor younger women who are in extreme situations. They helped me to cope with many issues.

It was through my membership in Keneyaton that an unexpected development occurred. I met another man. And after some time, got married again. This time I am the second wife of my current husband. We maintain separate households because of my children. My husband visits me occasionally. The home of his first wife is his primary residence. Initially, my second husband did not know about my seropositive status. I wanted to tell him, but the person at the clinic said not to do so, because there is a method to telling someone about your status.

I was told to reveal things to him in stages. I have told him that I was sick. I also used female condoms, so when he comes, he doesn't notice that I have the condom in. When I told him I had been ill, he didn't ask what condition I had. He only said, "No matter what the illness is, I love you." I have since told him about my HIV status, and he has subsequently been tested. He is negative. He has accepted me and my children. My current husband is a good man.

As for the issue of establishing an HIV support group for Muslims, I don't think it would be a sustainable idea. Because of stigma, such a group would be doomed before it began. It would be a hard thing to do in this country at this time.

I have not shared my seropositive status with my brothers, because I am not sure how they would take such information. I am glad I didn't have to tell our parents because I think it might have shamed them. Many people in Mali who belong to this era still don't believe there is such a thing as HIV or AIDS. Some who believe in the virus believe false information about it. Still others simply accept it as God's will or punishment for something they have done wrong. That was the view held by my first husband.

Although I have not shared my HIV status with my adult children, I have counseled them about how they must be careful in matters of sex and how to avoid contracting this virus. I have given them a lot of information. As far as they know, it has come from my association with Keneyaton. It is better for my sons and daughters not to know, especially my younger children. I would not want them to worry about me being ill.

Learning from HIV

Penda Diaby (pseudonym) is a Malian Muslim from Ségou. She is forty years old and is the first born of eight children. Ethnically, she is a Soninke.

I am from a family of eight. My mother is alive, but my father passed away a few years ago. I attended university and have a degree in architecture and building sciences. I was one of the few women in my class and I got used to hearing remarks like, "You won't get a husband because you are too educated." Part of my education was done abroad in France where I experienced many different perspectives and worldviews.

As a matter of fact, I was married, but my husband died of the virus. My husband, Jamil, was a wonderful young man. He was tall and strikingly dark skinned. We met as undergraduate students and just fell in love. He majored in engineering. We were so in love that when he was not around, I was sad. After completing his undergraduate degree, he had a successful career as a teacher and practitioner. But it is likely that he was seeing at least one other woman and no doubt contracted the virus from another sexual contact. I must emphasize "likely" because it is hard to imagine him with another woman. We were around each other so much that I can't figure out when he would have had the opportunity to meet someone else. I still believe that he might have contracted the virus some other way.

In any case, Jamil and I had an elaborate wedding with more than two hundred invited guests. Around 2007 or 2008, he began getting these unusual illnesses and they were coming quite routinely. It was strange for someone who was otherwise in terrific shape. Jamil continued to get these flus that seem to linger on. He also lost weight dramatically. His decline was progressive and debilitating. In April 2010, Jamil died. I felt like someone had cut my heart out.

I found out about my seropositive status in July 2010, months after Jamil's death. I loved him so much that it never occurred to me that he would have done this. I was devastated about losing him and really hurt about the HIV news. As I said, there is at least the possibility that he did not contract the virus via a sexual contact. Or if he contracted it sexually, it was before he and I were together. Jamil and I used condoms before marrying and afterwards for some time. We had agreed to delay children initially, so that I could establish my career. At a point in our marriage, we stopped using condoms because I was trying to get pregnant.

I was in total denial about the news of my seropositivity. After all, the people whom I had seen with this virus were impoverished. I suppose I saw it as a social class issue. In fact, I know that I did.

I became afraid of what this news would do to my mother, brothers, and sisters if this had come out. My parents had spent so much money on my wedding and my father had died before I could give him any grandchildren. I couldn't take this to my family on top of that. I was also afraid of being rejected by all of them. I was the oldest child and expected to set an example for my younger siblings.

It is only my mother who knows of my seropositive status. When I told her about it, she just hugged me. I felt like a child again. I know I cried like one. The only thing I received from her at that moment was motherly affection. I needed it desperately. Once I calmed down, she began laying out how we were going to handle this situation. Mother was measured and deliberate. That was her style and that's frankly what I wanted. My mother is the strongest woman that I have ever known. She could be stern, but I never doubted her love for me. She helped me to locate a clinic in October 2010 and went with me for the initial consultations and medical treatments. She had worked with several NGOs[1] and made some casual inquiries. I am grateful to have her.

After starting the treatment, an older man contacted my mother asking about my availability. He knew that I had lost my husband as a young woman and was interested to know if I had considered remarrying. He was fifteen years older than I was but was also a successful engineer. He had actually known Jamil. Remarrying was the last thing on my mind. After Jamil, I was a little shy about trusting men again. In any case, Seydou and I began courting and things became serious. We married three years ago. I am his second wife, but I maintain a separate household. Seydou and I don't have children, but his first wife has several. When I decided to remarry, my mother told me I didn't have to go through with it. She said I had already married and survived a dead husband, so there was no social pressure on me to marry again.

I am afraid to tell Seydou about my HIV status, because I do fear his rejection. I know that my education and career will allow me to work and support myself, but I didn't want to give up the chance of having a family. I will accept things either way.

---

1   Non-government Organizations

Because my viral load is now undetectable, I have been having unprotected sex with my husband. I may become pregnant eventually. I know I should tell him, but it will not be easy.

As for the possibility of forming a Muslim HIV support group, I don't see it as practical. There is still significant stigma here, even among educated Malians where HIV is concerned. Acquired Immune Deficiency Syndrome is still perceived as an illness for those with dubious or weak morals. Women are judged more harshly than men even though it is men who are far more likely to bring the virus to their wives or female partners. My mother is an exception when it comes to judging. She has enlightened herself about HIV and AIDS along with many other issues. Because of that, she is an exception to the rule.

Muslim men are definitely treated less harshly than women although they are mostly responsible. Men are less faithful, and our religion allows men to have more than one wife. Islam also makes it easier for a man to divorce a woman than the other way around. When a woman contracts HIV it is believed she is loose or immoral, but a man is not held to the same standard. When I studied in France, I saw a dramatic difference in how men and women interact on a more even basis. There is a significant Muslim population in that country, but you can still find many of the same views among Muslim men in France which are still prevalent in Mali.

I could see forming a woman's HIV support group where a newly infected woman is partnered with a coach or sponsor (i.e. a woman already in care) who tells the newly infected woman what she should expect and how to navigate certain situations. That is a more likely scenario than a men and women Muslim group.

Note – *Penda Diaby recently delivered twins. She had a girl and a boy. She maintains her career as an architect and also consults outside of Mali on various building projects.*

Vulnerability through Denial

Karitio Dembele (pseudonym) is a Malian Muslim from Ségou and is forty-five years old. She was one of eight children. Ethnically, she is a Minianka.

I am one of eight children and only one was a boy. Four of my sisters have passed away. One of my sisters was diabetic. I don't know what caused the deaths of the other three. Both of my parents are also gone. My father died in 2003 at ninety-seven years old and my mother died in 2013 in her eighties.

I went to school, but was forced to abandon it when I was about fourteen. My father withdrew me and made me marry. He was paid a sum of money, but I don't know how much. My husband was in the military and had been assigned to the northern part of Mali. He told my father that he needed a wife, because he would be stationed in the north for several years. So my father pulled me out of school to get married. I moved with my husband north to a military base in Gao. I was fifteen when this happened. I gave birth to my first child the following year. I now have a total of seven children - three sons and four daughters. All are HIV negative. My oldest son is twenty-nine years old and he has completed university. My youngest child does not belong to my first husband.

I was infected with HIV by my first husband. After Gao, he was assigned to another base in Sevare, which is also in the north close to Mopti. Thankfully, I had my children, because it was often lonely. I had all but lost routine contact with my family. One afternoon I was called to the base hospital because my husband had collapsed on a mission. After some initial treatment, he didn't get better. The military doctors performed an HIV test on him and he was positive, but never said anything to me about it at the time. I only found this out years later. He was subsequently discharged from the military for medical reasons, because his condition didn't improve enough to allow him to continue serving. My husband subsequently died. After his death, I found a letter that he had written to an old girlfriend, but it had not been mailed. In the letter he told this woman that he was dying of AIDS and that she should get tested. But he never admitted a thing to me. I had been his wife and the mother of his children. My husband's family actually believed that I had something to do with his death, so they rejected me and my children.

My friend who is a midwife told me to come and test for the virus and I did. I was so nervous to go that I was shaking from nervousness when my friend took me to the clinic where they drew my blood. I turned out to be positive. It was a very difficult period for me because my husband was already dead and in my mind I thought I was going to follow him to the grave. I still had young children and I was immediately concerned about who would take care of them.

I had heard of HIV from a distance, but I didn't believe it was true. I thought it was some made up disease that the U.S. or France had brought to Africa. At least that's what I heard. My midwife friend told me that I was not about to die, and went with me several times to the clinic. She said she knew of several women with the virus and had even helped to deliver many HIV positive women's babies. She said that when a seropositive woman took certain medication, their babies were just fine and didn't carry the virus. I was shocked to hear that.

I am now living back near my brother and sisters. One of my sisters knows of my positive status, but the others don't know. My mother knew about it before she passed away. She told me that she had resented and grew very bitter with my father for forcing me to get married so young. She said after I moved north, she felt like she had lost another one of her children. At the time, I know she was sad, but just couldn't do much about the situation. My sisters and brother have been supportive. I am at least grateful for that.

I married again a few years ago. I told my husband that I was HIV positive before we were married. I explained to him how I had contracted it from my first husband. I told him about my first husband's infidelity. I told him everything. It started as a general discussion about HIV and suddenly I opened up. He still wanted to marry me and be a father to my younger children. I thank God for him. Many men would have immediately run away from such a situation or rejected the woman outright. My youngest son belongs to him and because we conceived him following the directions we were given, my youngest son is also HIV negative. My husband and I still use condoms and every three months he tests for the virus. He has been negative every time.

I have since become involved with a group in Ségou known as Keneyaton which is like a support group, but not all of the women are HIV positive. They help women in a variety of ways.

I have counseled my older sons and daughters to be careful, because HIV is real. At a point in my life I didn't believe in it, but I do now. I also know you can live with this virus. I told my older children what happened to their father (my first husband). The older ones still remember how sick he was before he died.

I feel as though I have received another chance at life when my current husband married me. I feel doubly blessed because he became a father to my younger children. I have met several women in the association who have experienced terrible treatment at the hands of their husbands and families. Because I experienced some of that same treatment when my first husband's family accused me of having something to do with his death, I sympathize with these women who have been falsely accused or mistreated. I hope I can make a small difference in their lives.

CHAPTER 4

Surviving Shame

Rokia Diarra (pseudonym) is a Malian Muslim from Sikasso. She is twenty-eight years old and is the second born of four children. Ethnically, she is a Bambera.

There are four children in my family. There are three girls and a boy. We are all alive. My father died a year ago and my mother is still with us.

My childhood was difficult, because my father had a stroke as a result of his high blood pressure. Up until then, he provided for all of us very well. We were all expecting to matriculate at the university. When my father became paralyzed, my older sister and I had to abandon school to take care of him. I was thirteen years old and my older sister was fifteen. It was very traumatizing for us because it was as if our entire world was thrown into chaos. I went from being a part of an upper middle class background to selling water on the streets to help out our family.

I got married in 2006 at eighteen years old. I had a child before I married my husband. I became pregnant three times during my marriage, but each time I miscarried. My husband's parents started telling him to divorce me and find another wife. After losing the third child, I decided to see what was wrong with me physically. Included in my series of tests was an HIV test and that's when I found out I was seropositive.

I first heard about HIV during a preview at a movie theater, but I didn't pay much attention to it. Then I started hearing people around me talking about it. I suspected something was wrong after losing those three children.

When I found out my status, I was really worried because my father still needed my help. I thought it was the right thing for me to inform my husband of my status. Almost immediately, he ran off and told his mother and his father's second wife. They counseled him to divorce me on the grounds that I had been promiscuous and brought the virus into the marriage. In actual fact, it was my husband who gave me the virus. My first son who was born before I married my husband was and remains seronegative. I had him tested after I got my results. There was no sign of HIV in his system. My husband simply wanted to use his womanizing to blame the break up on me. It was an ugly thing that he did. There was a point when I actually considered suicide because of the shame that it brought to me and my entire family. It was painful.

My mother and father counseled me to come to the Walé Clinic in Ségou. I first spoke to a psychologist at the clinic who helped me to address some of the stress that I was dealing with. He said that if I didn't stop stressing myself, I would accelerate the progression of the HIV. My son also suffered because he saw the changes that were happening to me. I felt like I had been an awful mother.

I began a medical regimen to arrest the virus. I never became sick, because I started the treatment soon after learning of my seropositive status. I had a strong immune system overall.

After my husband divorced me, he remarried, but he must have infected that wife as well because I have seen her at the same HIV clinic. She and I have never gotten beyond courtesy greetings, but she knows who I am. I let it be known through a third party that my son and I were HIV negative before I married that man. Perhaps she will add two plus two. She doesn't have any children.

I worry now because I don't know if I will ever marry again. I am still young and now that I am in treatment, I believe that I am able to carry a child to full term. I hope that will be the case in the future.

Educated and Infected

Mary Thera (pseudonym) is a Malian Catholic woman from the Mopti region. She is twenty-two years old and is one of four children. Ethnically, she is a Bobo.

My father is a head master of a school and a deacon in our church. My mother works from home. She sews and makes clothing alterations. She is the one who gave me the love of sewing and designing clothes. All of my brothers and sisters graduated from secondary school and several of us have also attended university. After I graduated from university, I began training as a dress maker. I now specialize in designing high end women's formal wear.

I am single, but I am also two months pregnant. My boyfriend is a factory worker. I am on a course of Zidovudine to protect my unborn child.

I first heard of the Human Immunodeficiency Virus as a student in a biology course. The teacher told us about how the virus was contracted and spread. He said it came through infected blood contact, needle sticks in hospitals, through unprotected sex, and mother to child transmission. He also said that certain professions, like hospital workers who handled blood products, were at a greater risk of exposure. He dispelled several stereotypes like defecating in the same spot as a HIV positive person, or sleeping on the same bed as an HIV positive person could cause someone to contract it. The students asked many other questions, but I have forgotten them. Much of the discussion centered on protecting oneself from the virus. Although there were several females in the classroom, the focus was clearly on male condoms. I don't think the teacher had ever seen a female condom. He simply may not have known they existed. Most women and men do not. It was not until recently that I first saw one.

I found out about my HIV status a little over a year ago. My boyfriend started having these coughing spells and was losing weight noticeably. He had been a well-built man, but was also getting flu-like symptoms. He went to get tested, but said nothing to me. He kept totally quiet. Since we had been engaging in unprotected sex, I thought I should be tested as well. I was totally surprised about the results, because I had no symptoms at all. I didn't have any illness - not even a cough.

When I found out I was HIV positive, I just cried. I was mostly afraid about telling my parents. They had sacrificed for my education and I would have to take this to them. At the same time, I found out that I was pregnant with my boyfriend's child.

I eventually told my parents about my HIV status and my pregnancy. I first told my mother. I always went to her first with serious matters, because I knew she would provide a sympathetic ear. When I went to her, I immediately broke down in tears. I told her about the pregnancy first, and then the HIV. She just sat and listened to me without comment. As I knew she would, she said, "We must tell your father." I dreaded hearing those words, but I knew I had to.

My father was quite disturbed as I knew he would be. He wanted to immediately go to my boyfriend's family, but my mother wanted to wait and see if it was a viable pregnancy. We didn't tell my father about the HIV right away. Things have become a little calmer now. My boyfriend has been pretty quiet about things. There have been some expenses surrounding my pregnancy and my HIV treatment, but since my boyfriend is living at home with his parents, he has not contributed. I continue to work. Both of my parents believed that I should not stop work since I was not feeling sick. I don't see my boyfriend as often now. If he decides not to marry me, I have a right to limit his access to the child. My parents, especially my father, have become very negative about him. My mother mostly wants him to take responsibility for the child, even if we need to go to the court and force him to pay child maintenance.

Eventually I told my father about my HIV status. My father has had more of a problem with my pregnancy than my HIV status. When I told him about the virus, he told me that I was still his child no matter what. His reaction to the pregnancy was more difficult. He was already aware that HIV could be successfully treated and I have been very steadfast in taking my medication.

My father is still supportive of me and my career goals. He is not especially pleased with my boyfriend, but has insisted that he take responsibility for his child. He has been very firm about this.

Note – *In December 2015, Mary gave birth to a healthy baby boy. Her parents are thrilled with the addition to their family. Mary's boyfriend has offered to marry her, but she has refused the proposal at this point. Her father followed through to force her boyfriend to pay child maintenance in the court. Mary continues her work designing women's formal wear. Her mother babysits for her.*

CHAPTER 6

Stigma in a Small Village

Asiata Togola (pseudonym) is a Malian Muslim woman from the Ségou region. She is forty-one years old and is the fourth of nine children. Ethnically, she is a Bambera.

When I was young, my father worked in a factory making cars. He made a very good living for our family. When I was about nine or ten, he lost his job, so he took us to the village where he and my mother were from. I had been in school and doing very well up to that point, but after we moved to the village there was not enough room for me to attend school, so I was told. My name was placed on the school's waiting list for admission. The boys were given priority. So I stayed at home and waited. I had someone helping me with basic skills like reading, writing and mathematics, but eventually one year turned into two years and that into three years. At a point I decided not to go at all.

My parents stayed in the village, but I came to Ségou after getting married. My husband, Omar, is a trader. He came to the village to sell his goods which is how we met. We began a polite conversation and he eventually began courting me. We decided in 2014 that we should elope and not tell anyone. My parents eventually accepted it.

Omar was actually my third husband. My second husband, Mamun, had died. We don't know the real cause. Some wicked people in the village (including some in his family) believed that sorcery was somehow involved with Mamun's death. When an accusation like that occurs, the wife is under immediate suspicion. Some of his family asked if we had been getting along and asking other probing questions. One of his brothers consulted a traditional healer who came to my house and threw some orange colored liquid on it. That was supposed to determine if his spirit was still there. And if it was, the spirit would tell the living if his death was some kind of foul play. There was no follow up from the traditional healer, so I suppose he got whatever answer he was looking for.

There had been a growth on Mamun's neck. It was a large knot which gradually moved to his head. He refused to get treated for that knot on his head and that's what I believed eventually killed him in 2010. He and I had one son who was two years old when his father died. Our son had been sick from the time he was born. When my son with Mamun later became sick, the accusations resurfaced that I was some kind of witch. Eventually, I was able to get him in treatment and he is doing fine on medication.

When Omar offered me the opportunity to go, I was happy to leave the village. I only go there now to visit my parents and my brothers and sisters who are still there. I don't miss that place, because it was full of bad memories.

I married my first husband in 1997, and have a son from that relationship who was born in 1999. The father of my first son became positive after our son was born. My first husband tested for the virus and received a positive result, but kept quiet. He divorced me and I wasn't made aware of it until after the divorce had taken place. He remained in the village. To my knowledge, he is still there.

My current husband, Omar, knows of my HIV positive status. He too, is positive. We both get treatment at the same clinic in Ségou. My sisters know about my virus, but not my brothers. My parents are also aware of the situation.

The city is better for someone with HIV. In fact the city is better for people in a variety of ways. There is less judgement and fewer accusations and finger pointing. For example, if someone in the village made their HIV status known, they might not be rejected outright, but you would experience some form of social isolation. People would gradually move away from you and avoid your presence. I am guilty of the same behavior. I did it to draw attention away from myself. When I did it, I knew I was wrong, but I did it.

The stigma of this virus in a small village is a powerful one. I am glad I am no longer there. It became too stressful. People in that village automatically think you have done something wrong, especially if you are a woman who is seropositive. Most of the HIV positive women whom I have met tell me that it was their husbands or male partners who gave them the virus.

I have a seventeen year old son and he is currently living with my first husband. My son knows that his father and I are positive. I have counseled him to avoid contact with his father's blood. He travels to the clinic to get his father's medication and that's when I see him. My younger son doesn't know anything about all of this and wouldn't understand it at this point anyway. I will explain it to him when he is older. I take all of the appropriate precautions with him that I take for my older son.

CHAPTER 7

Alone, but not Abandoned

Djeneba Diakité (pseudonym) is a preliterate Malian Muslim woman from the Ségou region. She is twenty-five years old and was one of eleven children. Ethnically, she is a Peul.

We were a family of eleven brothers and sisters, but nine of my parent's children have died. There are only two of us. There is my younger brother and me. My father and mother are still alive. He was a professional driver, but is now retired. My mother has always been a homemaker. She hadn't gone to school and neither did I because I helped her at home.

I am single and have no children. I heard of HIV on the radio and television. When I was young I remember hearing about the sickness of some people and I heard the word, "AIDS," but I had no idea what it meant. It was after that experience that I heard about it on the radio and television. I was able to understand things a little better then.

When I was twenty-two, I went to the hospital for treatment of a severe flu. It was very bad and I started getting diarrhea. Nothing seemed to work. A doctor who I spoke to suggested that I get an HIV test. I did and received a seropositive result. I don't know how I became infected. I got married when I was thirteen years old.[1] It was an arranged marriage by my father. I had no choice in it. My husband was between twenty-two and twenty-five years old at the time. It was a first marriage for my husband as well. After the marriage, there was a quarrel over payment between my parents and my husband's family. My father eventually had the marriage dissolved, although it lasted about three years.

---

1   This does not always mean there was a formal marriage and might also refer to when the sexual debut took place.

After the marriage ended I moved back home with my parents. I occasionally sold clothes. I met another man and we were together for a few years. When he proposed that we marry, my father refused. There was another boyfriend after that, so I don't know who infected me. I have just accepted that it has happened. I wasn't afraid and I didn't panic. My brother's wife is also infected with the virus and she is not sick at all. She went to the Walé Clinic and got medicine. She is the one who told me about the clinic. I am able to do everything that I want to do. My brother's wife has been an example for me. She and I have become like sisters. We have been very supportive of each other.

I would like to get married again and have children. I now know it is possible. I believe it will happen for me if God wills it to be.

It's not that I am afraid to tell my parents about my seropositive status because I think they will reject me. It is because they have had eleven children and lost nine of them. If I were to tell my mother she, would panic and fear that she was about to lose one of her two remaining children. I don't want to put either of my parents through that experience again.

Marital Sacrifice

Sarah Coulibaly (pseudonym) is a Malian Muslim woman from the Ségou region. She is twenty-nine years old and was one of ten children with two different mothers. Each of her father's wives had five children. Ethnically, she is a Bambera.

I am the second born of my mother. My father is retired from the military. I received my high school diploma, but did not proceed to university. I am married with two children. I have an eleven year old son from a previous relationship, and a daughter who is now four.

I first heard about HIV through hearing these two old women gossiping about some young woman who, according to them, was "promiscuous." Her loose behavior, they said, had led to her getting the "sickness." I actually knew the girl whom these old women were gossiping about. I knew the girl's older sister and she had told me that her younger sister had been abandoned by a young man who had promised to marry her. Anyway, these old women were saying that when you got this virus, you would get sick and die. I vaguely remember something about "positive" which didn't make sense at the time. The women eventually became aware that I was paying attention to them and one of them said that's what happened when women were sexually unfaithful. I also remember hearing things on the radio and television. We got practically no exposure to this virus, or, for that matter, any basic sex education as a part of our educational training.

My husband is in the military. Before our marriage, I could get anonymous testing because of his military service. When I tested and received a positive resul' I was surprised and afraid. I thought my world was about to unravel entirely. I was 2012. I told him about my HIV positive status, but he said it didn't matte to him. He wanted us to be together. I really loved my then fiancé, but I tol him he didn't have to go through with the wedding. He refused to let me go, so the marriage took place as planned one month after I received my seropositive result. My husband received counseling in the military about certain precautions to take during our marital relations. We went to see a specialist who put me on medication after I became pregnant. When I gave him a daughter, we were both extremely happy. Somehow, I thought there would be some complication with the pregnancy. Now that I know I can successfully carry a child to term, I would like to give my husband one or two sons. My baby daughter is HIV negative. We did the test on her after she was born. There was another test when she was six months old and then the final one was done after she reached eighteen months. By then her immune system was fully functioning.

My parents don't know of my seropositive status. My husband decided that we should not share any of those details and I will respect his decision. I don't want to harm his career in any way. He was and remains HIV negative. There is no way for me to repay him for the sacrifice that he made to be with me. I hope to be able to give him the sons that he deserves. All of our relations are protected until we attempt to conceive again.

I will explain things to my son when he is older. He is not ready for such a serious conversation at this point in his life.

CHAPTER 9

Transcending the Blame

Miriam Dena (pseudonym) is a Malian Muslim woman from Sikasso. She is thirty-six years old. She is the sixth born of nine children. She has seven sisters and one brother. Ethnically, she is a Bobo.

My parents are still alive. My father is seventy-six and my mother is about seventy. My husband is dead. I have a seventeen year old daughter and an eleven year old son. I went to school in Ségou from the age of seven and did quite well.

I remember hearing whispers about this "SIDA/HIV" (HIV/AIDS) in secondary schools, but it was mostly hearing kids joke about the virus. Some of them were making jokes about the virus and saying outlandish things like if a boy caught it, the virus would make his genitals shrink up and fade away. He would then have to live life as a woman. As far as women were concerned, it would make your breast grow prematurely and sag like you were an old woman. And, you could not have children.

I was engaged at fifteen, but my parents insisted that I be allowed to finish my secondary education before marrying. They had allowed the engagement to take place under those conditions. Both families agreed to the terms. The man I married, however, became HIV positive and he contaminated me. When we first married, he was HIV negative. I know that because I have two children with him. I have a daughter seventeen and an eleven year old son. Both are HIV negative.

My husband became sick and died after a prolonged series of illnesses. After he died, I began getting these colds and flu-like symptoms. I just assumed that I was suffering after having nursed him for so long. In 2013, one of my sisters sensed that it was more serious than that and suggested that I get an HIV test. She had

ing about my late husband having another woman. I followed her
it's how I found out that I was HIV positive. Even though he was
om being a grieving widow to an angry woman. I was very bitter.
and had never said a word to me about why he was ill. I wonder if he
my knew the cause of his sickness. All I could think was that he let me become
infected and died keeping quiet. I sometimes still struggle with that anger in my
mind.

I even resented his family, because I thought some of them had known of
his health condition. Once, I nearly came close to hurling abuses at them, but that
would have reflected negatively on me and my children. Instead, we just left that
family compound and moved back in with my family. His parents didn't want us
to leave and wondered if something had occurred to make us feel unwelcomed. I
really didn't give a good explanation for my departure, because I was so embittered.
His family was very close to my son and daughter. Taking them away from my
in-laws was difficult for everyone.

I have since reconciled with my late husband's family although they still don't
know the reason why I was angry at them. Once I reflected on it, my husband may
not have told them either. It's the society that we live in. Had I told my husband's
family that he died of this deadly infection, they might have accused me of killing
him. That kind of accusation is still common in our country.

I have to say in total honesty that his family has been helpful to my children.
My daughter will complete high school and receive her diploma next year. My late
husband's family has offered to assist with her university training should she do
well in her exams.

My parents came to know about my seropositive status shortly after I came
back home. I didn't want to place them in an unsafe situation, so I explained that
it was my husband who had infected me years after we had been married. My
father actually asked for my forgiveness, because he thought my late husband had
been a decent man and a good provider. He had been, all things considered. In
any case, they immediately accepted me and my children back in their home. My
mother asked if my son and daughter were okay, because they would be around
other children in the family their age. I told her that they were both HIV negative
because I had them tested (using the oral test). My parents have been remarkably
helpful to me.

Recently, I have told both of my children about my HIV status. I explained
that it was their father who had given me the virus and that is what he died of.
I also told them that he may not have known of his infection because it can take
years to emerge after the initial infection. I didn't want to harm his name in their
eyes. He was their father and it would have done no one any good for them to
harbor ill will against him. He, in many ways, was a product of his environment
and our society.

I explained to my children in order to avoid infection, they must not have
unprotected sex. I also explained about being careful about coming in contact with
other people's blood, because you don't know if it is infected or not.

Considering where I am emotionally at this point to where I was when I first learned of my infection, I feel like a very different person. I am in a better place. I am not too old to marry again, but it would have to be to someone who would accept me as I am and be honest with me. I would also insist on knowing their serostatus before marrying. At that point, I would disclose my status.

My eyesight has degenerated a little because of the virus, but that is the only effect that I have noticed. I am currently taking Atripla which is one pill a day. I have a few pains here and there, but am in good shape overall.

CHAPTER 10

Social Status, Security and HIV

Ami Cissé (pseudonym) is a Malian Muslim woman originally from Mopti. She is forty-three years old. She is the sole daughter among five siblings. Ethnically, she is a Peul/Fulani.

My mother is still alive, but my father has been dead for several years. I have been married twice and have been a first and second wife. I have two sons - one by each of my husbands. My oldest son (whose father is dead) is a university student. I have a younger son from my second marriage who is now six.

Shortly after my first husband, Ousman, and I married in late 1994, we moved to Dakar, Senegal. He worked as a manager for an international import/export company. Our son, Husseini, was born in 1995. He attended international school where he learned to speak French, English, and Wolof. We were very happy and prosperous in Senegal. Because of Ousman's outstanding job performance, we were able to help family members back in Mali and made regular trips back as a family. Today, my oldest son speaks English and French better than he speaks Bamanankan. Ousman had worked so hard, he advanced to become the senior manager for his company. He was outgoing, reliable, and the employees loved him because he was so generous to them. Even on occasions when he had to terminate someone, he brought them in and explained how this decision had been reached. They may not have liked the decision, but they respected him for his diplomacy and integrity.

After my son turned five, Ousman started having periodic illnesses. Some of these illnesses were debilitating and he missed days at work. This was very difficult for him because he worked very hard and felt that if he was not at his job, things would not work properly. Ousman felt like he was not living up to his responsibilities as a husband and provider.

As Ousman received promotions within his company, his job responsibilities increased and he also began traveling to Europe and spent more time away from home. I went with him on a few of these trips in which wives were allowed. One of these trips on which I accompanied him was to New York City. I suspect that it was on one of these European trips that Ousman was infected with this virus.

In any case, his health continued to decline. In 2002 after months of debilitating illness, my dear Ousman died. I immediately informed our families back in Mali of his death. Since his company paid all of the funeral expenses, we decided to bury Ousman in Senegal. He had made his burial arrangements prior to his death. At the time that we had that discussion, he said he could save money. Shipping his remains back home, according to him, would be an unnecessary expense. The company closed for the funeral observance and several of his bosses traveled from France and other parts of Europe to attend. He was held in such high regard as an employee. Two of his brothers flew in, but his parents were too old and devastated to come and bury their son. My son, Husseini, was still a young boy.

Before he died, however, Ousman had arranged financially for Husseini and me to stay in Senegal, which we did until my son completed his primary school education. We then moved back to Mali in 2005. Aside from leaving me with a generous widow's pension, Ousman's company guaranteed financing our son's education from private secondary school through his university studies regardless of where he was admitted.

It was also that year that I received my HIV positive diagnosis. I did not have any symptoms, but a doctor in Dakar who knew the cause of Ousman's death diplomatically suggested that I be tested for the virus. I avoided it for some time, but eventually tested and received the results. After taking in the information, I was resolved to be a good mother to my son and to honor the memory of my deceased husband. I wasn't angry with Ousman. He had given me and my son a very good life and made it possible for us to live comfortably after his death.

I continued my treatment once I resettled back in Mali and was keenly aware of the importance of taking my daily medications. Once, I ran low on my pills which were usually delivered to me by courier. The courier scheduled to deliver the medication on this particular occasion got into a motor bike accident and didn't show up. I called my private physician who said he could arrange for me to get the medication at a clinic that he was affiliated with, but I would need to go in person for verification purposes. I was petrified at that idea, because I just knew someone there would recognize me. I dressed down and made my way to the clinic wearing a scarf.

When I sat with the other women at the clinic whom I assumed were also there for similar treatment, I became very nervous. I held my head down, and gave the name of one of brother's wives to disguise my identity. As I was going into an office to give more information, I bumped into a man carrying what sounded like a box with pills in it. When we collided, I knocked the box out of his hand and I could hear something shaking inside. He appeared to be just as nervous as I was. When I bent down to pick up his box, keeping my head down as much as possible, he quickly grabbed it, apologized for the accident and moved away very quickly. I noticed that he was wearing very expensive shoes when I glanced down at his feet. The shoes didn't match the rest of what he was wearing.

Sometime later, the imam at the mosque that my son and I attended wanted me to meet a man who was new to the area. He described him as financially well-situated and thought I might like to meet him. Reluctantly, I agreed just to be courteous. When our eyes met, we both recognized each other from the clinic. It was the same man I had accidently bumped into there. Just to confirm things, I glanced down at his feet and he happened to be wearing the same expensive shoes that he had on when we hastily avoided each other months earlier. Neither of us, however, indicated any prior knowledge of the other at that time. Our conversation was courteous and polite. After a short time, my son came to join me. He asked who the man was. I simply introduced him as a friend.

Over the next several months, Musa and I got to know each other better. We eventually had a conversation about how, where, and under what circumstances we had first met. We actually had a real laugh at how nervous both of us were that day and wanted to be anywhere but that clinic. He too had dressed down to disguise himself while in that hospital clinic as had I. I told him that I knew he was out of place because of his shoes. Once the discussion of our mutual seropositive status was out of the way, things really began to develop between us. From that point on, there were no secrets that we didn't share. I told him about Ousman and he told me he also had a wife. Musa and I eventually agreed that we should marry. But I explained that I would keep and maintain my separate house. I also said that he needed to respect the memory of my son's father. Before long, however, Husseini started to call him, "Papa," which is what children educated in the French tradition called their fathers.

In 2009, Musa and I were blessed with a son. It was my second child and his fourth. We were both overjoyed about this birth. Because we had followed the medical directions before and during my pregnancy, our baby son eventually tested as HIV negative. I must say, this was the most beautiful baby, because I regarded him as a miracle. I never thought that I could be any happier than having this precious little boy. He was such a healthy and delightful baby. He seemed to cry very little and always had a smile on his precious tiny face.

Three years after the birth of our son, however, tragedy struck. My dear beloved Musa was killed in a motor accident while traveling home. A truck had struck his car. He and his driver were killed. When I heard the news, I just collapsed. We were all devastated. In a certain way, Musa's death hit me harder than Ousman's. At least I had preparation for that death. I had nursed him and seen his health decline. Musa's death was sudden with no warning. Husseini had been young when his father died, so Musa had become, for all practical purposes, his father. Musa's death hit him very hard as well. He was the only father that Husseini had known.

Musa and I had fought HIV together and that created yet another special bond between us. I was fully expecting to spend my senior years with this man. I routinely tell my six year old son today that his daddy was a special man. My older son continues to refer to him as "Papa."

* * * * *

All of my brothers know about my HIV status. As their only sister, they somehow feel obliged to protect me. I don't try to hide it now. My economic status has, in many ways, shielded me from certain kinds of indignities and social isolation that I might have otherwise experienced. I remember an incident where one of my brother's wives had told one of her children not to touch a plate that I had handled. I informed my brother about it and he confronted her. His wife came to me in tears and apologized. I didn't make much of it, but I explained to her that the virus could not be passed on that way. It was a polite enough conversation.

At some point we might be able to have an HIV Muslim support group in this country, but we are not yet there. I think in Bamako it will be easier than in a rural area.

I am busy raising my young son. His older brother is now in the university. The young one really looks up to his brother. My older son took his young brother to the campus once and he stayed there for two nights in the hostel. My young son came back a changed boy. He wants to be just like his older brother.

I have been very direct with my older son in discussing protected sex and his relationships. I believe he will listen. He is such a fine young man. I could not ask for a finer and more respectful son. Thankfully, he has my brothers and Ousman's brothers who have all been father figures for him. In other words, he is surrounded by many well respected and responsible men.

I have become estranged from Musa's first wife and her children. I heard there were whispers about me having now buried two husbands, there must have been something unnatural about it. There was not a formal rift between the families as such, but I always sensed that there was some resentment from her. I am convinced there was also some dissatisfaction regarding the disposition of Musa's estate. I think she believed she should have inherited more than she did. I also think she resented Musa including Husseini in his will even though he was not my son's birth father. I was actually surprised by that inclusion as well, but that was the nature of the man. I also believe there was some long-held envy on her part about my economic independence and the fact that both of my children have gone to private schools and my oldest son is now a university student. I saw one of her daughters recently and she looked in the opposite direction when I called out to her. It is a shame, but fortunately I have a supportive family structure that has embraced me and my sons. Frankly, I will be content if I don't marry again. I do look forward to becoming a grandmother at some point in the future. God willing, it will happen.

I recognize that we lose many men and women in this country because of our unwillingness to speak about the virus. When my younger son gets older, I plan to become more involved in HIV awareness campaigns. But as for now, I don't want him to suffer any hardships from his peers because of me.

CHAPTER 11

Perseverance and Faith

Rebecca Kansaye (pseudonym) is a Malian Christian woman (a Protestant) originally from Mopti. She is preliterate and her age is unknown, although she appears to be in her fifties. She is an only child. Ethnically, she is a Dogon.

My mother and father had one other daughter, but she died years ago. They have since passed away. I went to school, but left when I was about six or seven years old, as I remember. I was married when I was sixteen years old, but my husband has been dead since 2008 or 2009. He was killed in the Ivory Coast. His father was an Ivorian and his mother is Malian. Because of his father, my late husband had dual citizenship and served in the Ivory Coast military. We lived in that country with our five children. All, but one of my children were born there. I believe they may be eligible for Ivorian citizenship since their father was a national.

My husband was killed in the civil and political unrest in the country leading up to one of the elections. The conflict had gone on for a few years before my husband was killed. I believe he was killed, because of his dual Ivorian/Malian citizenship. He had been accused of being a spy despite being in the military. His death might have also been religiously motivated, because, like me, he was also a Christian.

When I was informed of his death, my children and I had to go into hiding. I never saw his body. There was no funeral to my knowledge. I also have no idea where his final resting place is. Because of that, I believe even today his soul is not at rest. That has haunted me for years now.

My children and I had to secretly cross the border back into Mali. We traveled mostly at night. I am told that there are benefits in the Ivory Coast that I am entitled to, because of my husband's military service. But I am too afraid to return to that country.

When I came back to Mali after leaving the Ivory Coast, my children and I made our way straight to Mopti to my husband's parents. My husband's sister said that we must go away. She said the family could not take me and my children in. So we migrated to Ségou. It was a very difficult time for my children and me.

I heard about this virus called "AIDS," on the streets, but I didn't know much about it. People said it also had something to do with blood. I heard a woman community leader say that you could get it by washing clothes. Since that is how I made my living after moving to Ségou, I believe that's how I contracted the virus. I am sure I have washed the clothes of many of those infected and got the virus from one of them. I know that sexual relations can cause the virus as well, but I haven't been with another man since the death of my late husband.

I began having a cough a few years after my husband's death. Sometimes I would also get a fever. It may have been around 2011. I went to see a traditional healer who gave me some medication, but it made me vomit. I went to two more healers and they didn't help either. After many treatments, I wasn't getting better. The final healer suggested that I go to a clinic for an HIV evaluation.

After getting to the clinic I was evaluated and tested. Then I was also told that I was HIV positive. When I told the counselor that I washed other people's clothes for a living and believed that's how I got the virus, she said that it was likely that I got it from my husband or perhaps through a cut or coming in contact with someone's blood. When I told her that my husband had been dead for several years and I had not been with another man, she said it could take years for someone with the virus to become sick. Like I said, I got married when I was sixteen and have only been with my husband. So, I was not entirely sure I believe the counselor, so I left that clinic.

I came to the Walé Clinic as a result of having done the laundry for a children's foundation. The man who works at the foundation office wrote a note for me to present to Walé. I came here and got my previous diagnosis confirmed. When I realized what was being said, I asked if I could get HIV from having washed so many clothes. The doctor told me I couldn't get it that way. The next thing I said was if I should die, who would look after my children. I was close to tears. I am an only child and my parents are dead I told him. I didn't want my children to be orphans. I told him that my late husband's family had rejected me. There was only me. The doctor told me that once I started the medication and remained faithful to that treatment schedule, I would be fine and could continue working.

Once I got sick I received a visit from my husband's sister. This was the same sister who had sent me and my children away when we needed help. When I told her my sickness was HIV, she left. It is only me with my five children. I rent a small flat and pay at the end of each month.

My oldest daughter is now fifteen. That was the age when I was promised to a man. And within months, I was married. I pray that my daughter will have an easier time than I have had. Thankfully, all of my children are HIV negative. I have since had my two sons circumcised at the clinic because I was told that it would help to protect them from the virus.

Now, I wash and iron clothes worry-free. I am taking care of my health and looking after my children. I also belong to a church and that has been a major source of comfort. The pastor and other members have even helped to get me other clients. I now have so many clients that I had to hire four other women to help with the laundry work. I have done well enough to move into a larger place with my family. My oldest daughter has begun working in the business as well. She does a very good job ironing and folding clothes. Through Our Lord Jesus Christ all things are possible. There are still challenges, but I didn't expect to live this long.

Note – *At the advice of a church member, Rebecca Kansaye consulted an attorney and had her husband officially declared dead in the Ivory Coast. She is in the process of filing paper's to receive a widow's pension for herself and her children. She has also received another large contract to do laundry for another hotel in Ségou and has added two additional workers. Her goal is to educate her children including having them to attend university.*

CHAPTER 12

Motherhood Robbed

Djelika Kouyate (pseudonym) is a Malian Muslim woman originally from Koulikoro. She is forty-five years old and is preliterate. She is one of nine children. Ethnically, she is a Malinke.

I am the third born of my parent's nine children. Three of us have died. I am not sure of the cause. My father was in his sixties when he passed away. My mother is now in her sixties. She started having children when she was fourteen.

I never went to school. I am the mother of five children. I had three girls and two boys. The oldest, a girl, is twenty-five and my youngest child is thirteen. I am divorced from my children's father. He divorced me when he learned of my HIV status, and took away my children. He did this when I was still nursing my youngest son. After he left, I was told that I needed to phone before attempting to see my children, so I was forced to sneak to see them.

I remember begging him to let me continue to nurse my youngest child. My former husband at least agreed to that. It was the most painful experience that a mother can ever have – to be separated from her children. Even now it is a struggle for me to maintain a relationship with them. I am here with my one year old grandson. He is a beautiful boy. He is the son of my oldest daughter. Her father doesn't know he is with me. My daughter told him that he is with another parent. I have had to have a secret relationship with my children for more than ten years. I hope that they at least know their mother cares about them and I always will.

The irony of this is that my former husband brought the virus to me and then accused me of wrong doing. I first heard of this virus when I was told to come here to the clinic. I was sick and went to several traditional healers without success. One of the healers said that she had seen so many people with these symptoms that she believed this illness had been sent by the ancestors. Finally, one of the traditional healers suggested that I come here to the hospital in Ségou. When I came back, I was shown an animation (cartoon) about how HIV is contracted and spreads. At the time, the clinic also put on short plays to illustrate how women could protect themselves. They took place every Tuesday, but because of funding they have stopped them. After my HIV status was confirmed, I was told by a counselor that I needed to inform my husband, because it was likely that he was also infected. When I informed him as I was told to, he struck me and then left. Sometime later, I received a notice that he had divorced me and was taking my children. There was nothing that I could do. I have since been told that I was entitled to have routine and regular visitations with my children and it was against the law for him to have denied me from seeing them. I didn't know any better. Because he was more educated than I am, he lied and told me the law was on his side. A lawyer told me that he needed to have proved in a court (civil or Islamic court) at the time that I was an unfit mother. He had no such evidence as that.

* * * * *

I have since remarried. My second husband is also seropositive. We met at the hospital's clinic. The doctors here explained how we need to protect ourselves during our marital relations. He has been married three times before and has lost at least two wives to the virus. But he is now taking his treatment along with me. He also has three grown children and a teenage daughter.

As far as my children are concerned, I have been very direct with them about my virus, especially the older ones. Despite my first husband's wickedness, I have remained a strong presence in their lives. I am grateful to this clinic for helping me to live. It actually saved my life and gave me a new one with another husband.

Note - *Djelika Kouyate's first husband is very ill and wanted to see her as he is reportedly near death. As of this writing, she has refused to see or speak to him.*

CHAPTER

13

Unknown Origin

Fatimata Keita (pseudonym) is a Malian Muslim woman originally from Niono. She is thirty-four years old and is preliterate. She is one of twelve children. Ethnically, she is a Malinke.

I had eleven siblings (from two marriages of my father). There are now nine of us alive (six boys and three girls). Both of my parents are still alive. My father may be about eighty and my mother is in her seventies, but I am not totally sure. They live in Koutiala.

I didn't go to school, but I did four years of training at the Islamic school between the ages of eight and twelve.[1] I left when I was twelve because my father could no longer afford the fees for my schooling, so I helped my mother at home.

I was married and had a daughter, but she died. After that, my husband and I divorced. In 2010, I found out I was HIV positive. I told my former husband that he should also test, but he refused. He and I simply could not reach an understanding and things between us have since grown very bitter.

When our daughter was born, she was constantly sick. I didn't know my seropositive status at the time, so I unknowingly passed the virus on to my child. I had no way of knowing what had caused her illness. My poor little girl lingered on for nearly three years before dying. She was constantly ill. I consulted several healers, but they were unable to help her. Although she was nearly three years old when she died, she looked more like a one year old infant. I think my little girl's death put me in a depression.

---

1   Islam school is akin to a madrasa which is a school where young men study the Islamic religion.

After that, I started to become ill. I remembered that when I was small, I saw people who had the same symptoms that I had. I had no idea how I had gotten sick unless it came from my child. One of my husband's sisters died shortly thereafter and I heard the term "AIDS" (literally "SIDA") whispered as the cause of her death. I saw her lose hair and she also had rashes. I was beginning to have some of the same symptoms. When I finally got tested and learned of my seropositive status, I thought to myself, "I am dead." I couldn't eat, or sleep. I couldn't do anything.

I cannot say exactly that it was my husband. I also had a boyfriend. When I learned more about how the virus can be contracted, I remembered that my mother used needles to pierce the arms, heads, hands, and necks of me and my sisters. She did this for many other women and girls. She often used the same needle to pierce several of her clients including me. There is a chance that I was infected that way. I can't be entirely sure. I know I became sick in my mid-twenties. This means there is a chance that I infected my former husband, but since he has not tested to my knowledge I can't say for sure.

I have spoken to my mother about getting tested, but so far she had refused to do so. She says that God will decide her fate. I don't know how to bring the issue of HIV testing up to my sisters who have also been pierced without them wondering why I would be asking such a question. I fear that they will become suspicious of me. I know there has to be a way of approaching them about this, but I am just not sure what to do.

One of the counselors at the clinic suggested that I gather all of my sisters together and that we come to the clinic as a group. That way, all of them could be anonymously tested and only they would know the results. I have to at least try. I think that if I say nothing and I lose one of them to this virus, God forbid, I would be condemned for my silence, not to mention my guilt for having said nothing.

CHAPTER 14

Living in Reality

Sitan Kane (pseudonym) is a Malian Muslim woman originally from Ségou. She is forty years old and is preliterate. She was one of twelve children. Ethnically, she is a Somono. Her mother had died just two weeks before our meeting.

I am one of twelve children. Only five of us are still alive. My father died years ago and my mother just died. My parents moved my older brother and sister and me to Lomé, Togo when I was about five. I didn't go to school while I was there. I grew up in that country and did not return to Mali until I was twenty. I spoke Kabye and Mina (both of which are dialects of Ewe) fluently while growing up in Togo. After returning to Mali twenty years ago, I started to lose my fluency in those languages.

When I came back to Mali, my parents had arranged for me to marry. My father's sister's son (i.e. my first cousin) became my husband. I had not met anyone in that family and certainly didn't know the cousin I was to marry. He and I married and I had eight children. Four of them have passed away and four are still alive. My oldest son is thirteen and the youngest is just over one. (Sitan Kane was carrying the sleeping one year old son on her back during our meeting.)

My four children who died lived less than three years after their births.[1] They were so young. It was very traumatic for me, but I came to accept it as the will of God.

I actually heard about HIV while I was living in Togo and remember being told that it was some kind of wasting illness. I was informed that people who got

---

1   This was possibly the result of Sudden Infant Death Syndrome (SIDS).

it lost weight and came to look like zombies. I believed, at the time, that it was something that the foreign tourists had brought to Africa from France or some other European countries. In 2001, my husband started getting ill with several symptoms like weight loss and he also had a persistent cough. We decided to travel to Bamako so he could see a doctor there. After several tests, they did an HIV test and determined that he was seropositive. Because he was positive, the doctor also wanted to test me to see if I was also seropositive. I was twenty-five years old at the time that I learned that I was HIV positive.

We were referred to the Walé Clinic back in Ségou by the hospital in Bamako. Both of us received counseling. We have since had three more children and all of them are HIV negative.

My oldest son is starting to show signs of manhood. I think he should be given advice about sexual relationships and HIV. I will definitely inform my daughters about how the virus spreads and how to prevent it from entering their bodies. I will tell them when they are old enough to understand.

Although I did not know enough to prevent my contracting HIV, I am a witness that you can live with this virus. As I said, I have had three children since my diagnosis and I may have one more child. What is important is that my husband and I looked reality in the face and we both got treatment. There is no anger between us. There is only the feeling of responsibility to our children. And we are grateful that we are able to be here for them. Anyone can die. It can be an accident in a car, or some other deadly illness. But my husband and I can tell you that you don't have to die from HIV or AIDS. There are many other things in life that are much worse than this illness.

I would counsel anyone with this virus to faithfully take their medicine. I know several people who got the news of their seropositive status and immediately thought their lives were about to end. It isn't always easy to remember your medication, but I have only forgotten to take mine once in all these years. The doctors in Bamako and Ségou have been very good. They never mentioned death. They simply told us how to live with this infection. I must say that this experience has brought me and my husband closer together. He is a wonderful father to our children and oddly enough I believe it is because of the HIV.

CHAPTER 15

Disclosure by Force

Assanatou Bouare (pseudonym) is a Malian Muslim woman originally from Ségou. She is thirty years old. She is one of seventeen children (produced by two wives). Ethnically, she is a Bambera.

There are seventeen children in my family. Ten are from my father and mother who was his first wife. His second wife had seven. My mother had six boys and four girls. I am the youngest of my mother's children. My father passed away some years ago, but my mother is still alive.

I left school when I was seventeen. I have since married and have three children. My oldest daughter is twelve and I have two younger sons. My husband is a psychology counselor for an HIV agency. He is also HIV positive.

I became infected in 2002 when I was about seventeen. It came from a sexual contact I had then. I was promised in marriage to a man and he likely infected me through our sexual activity. When I got the results of the test, I thought I was going to die. That's what people said at the time. I did the HIV test as I was preparing to marry. I went with some other girls, because we all decided to get tested. We believed it was the socially responsible thing to do. I was totally stunned by the results when I received the news more than a week later.

Practically everyone came to know of my seropositive status. My parents, sisters, brothers all knew, and it was not because I told them. I was forced into doing so. After I took the test and got my results, the psychologist here at the clinic told me I should inform my fiancé of my seropositive status. The counselor said he needed to know. I informed him and he decided to break off the marriage. He told his parents that I was positive and he didn't stop there. He told everyone he knew about my status. It was mostly to divert attention from him for having infected me. I had not been with any other man before him. I felt publically humiliated and shamed.

Fortunately, none of my family had a negative reaction to my seropositive status. Supposedly, my former fiancé did the test and was told he was negative, but I suspect he has not been truthful. He was merely trying to blame me for what he had done.

The man that I later married, as I said, is also positive. I am his first wife and he now has a second wife. She too is positive. My three children, however, are negative. Our last born, who is now ten months old, tested positive just after his birth, but we were told that this was likely to happen. He has since tested negative now that his immune system has begun functioning properly. He will be tested one more time at eighteen months and he should be fine after that.

There are still many people in this country who do not believe HIV is real. Many consult traditional healers. Some of the healers falsely promise cures to the virus, only to worsen the patient's condition. Some of it has to do with our educational system which does not teach our young people properly about male/female relationships, and how they should protect themselves. It is left to the family or someone else to teach that kind of information and it isn't always accurate. Sometimes it is not done at all.

I believe that a Muslim support group like that in South Africa might work, but it will take some level of exposure. And those of us who are seropositive must face up to the reality that being HIV positive is not a crime and it doesn't make you an immoral person. In Mali, we are not yet at that stage. Oftentimes people use our religion to cast aspersions on others in the name of God. I have certainly suffered from those kinds of accusations. I also know, after going into treatment, that you can live with this virus, have a family, and see your children grow and develop. I stand as a witness of someone who has done it.

CHAPTER 16

Forgiveness Can Heal

Nana Konate (pseudonym) is a Malian Muslim woman originally from Sikasso. She is twenty-nine years old and is one of seven children. Ethnically, she is a Malinke.

I am the third born of seven children. My parents had three girls and four boys. I went to school, but I had to stop early because my father believed it wasn't important for a girl to be educated. He felt that an educated daughter would be harder to marry and she would also be too selective. This meant there was a chance she would be alone. So my father made me stop. I picked up some things here and there, and learned how to read and write my name. And with the help of a tutor, I advanced even further. The tutor told me that I could have gone much further had I had the opportunity to stay in school. My brothers, on the other hand, were allowed to go to school, but not the girls. We were encouraged to stay at home.

I was finally married in 2008 and have since given birth to three children. They are seven, two, and one. I am also my husband's only wife. My husband is in the military and we have lived in several places throughout the country. At a point, he was deployed to northern Mali and I didn't follow him there because of security issues.

A neighbor first told me about AIDS and how people who had it got sick and died. My response to all of this was that it wasn't true. It could not be real.

When my second child was born, I needed blood. The hospital analyzed my blood and then sent for my husband. They asked to test him for something as well. It was he who told me he was infected with HIV and so was I. I didn't understand what he was saying, because I only had one husband and as far as I know, I am his only wife. He is the only man that I have ever known. I thought because I was in labor at the time, I was not following the conversation properly. It wasn't until after I had given birth that what he had said began to make sense.

I was told that my baby would need to have medicine so he would not be infected. Thank God, he now tests negative. Unfortunately, my first child is infected with the virus. We found that out the same time that my husband and I found out our statuses. My older son is now receiving medication. I have since had another child and she is also negative.

When I first realized that I was seropositive, I was afraid. I had a young child and a new baby. I thought I would die and leave them without a mother. My husband took us to meet a specialist who told us that we would be okay, but we needed to enter into care. He really made me feel calm when he explained that not only was I not going to die, I would be able to raise my children and take them to school and have more children if that's what I wanted!

I don't know the name of the medication that my husband and I take, but it initially made me dizzy. I was told this could be a side effect. My oldest son is on a different medication. The doctor switched my husband and me to another treatment, because it was making both of us unsteady. We now take two pills a day instead of one.

We have decided to keep our seropositive status within our immediate family, so no one knows about it. We decided that was the easiest way to maintain our daily lives. The doctor told us not to inform our oldest child about the virus, because he is too young. He takes his medication and we have explained to him that our family takes vitamins to stay healthy. I tell him that his father takes them and I take them.

When I came to know how HIV is contracted, I was ready to accuse my husband for bringing me this virus. He was so pitiful and remorseful, that I couldn't stay angry with him. When he suggested that we could deal with this as a family, I decided to forgive him. We are together and I hope we will remain so for the balance of our lives.

The idea of a Muslim HIV support group is a good idea, but in the current situation not an easy process to initiate. My guess is that most seropositive people in this country would rather not disclose their status. I would even imagine that if someone was seen going in and out of an HIV clinic, they are likely to still deny their seropositive status. People here are more likely to just keep quiet.

There is the matter of my husband and I telling our oldest son of his HIV status. I think we will wait until he is eighteen. I know there is a chance that he will become sexually active before then, but if I tell him too soon, what would be the reaction if he tells his friends? They might reject him as well as his younger brother and sister thinking that they are also positive. One of the counselors suggested that I have a psychologist speak to him as he approaches his teen years and explain things to him. I know he will come to have the desires of a man. I worry at this point if he cuts himself and bleeds that can also be a problem, but I just don't want to burden him too soon with this situation. My children are all so young. I just don't know. Perhaps there will be a cure for this disease by the time my children come of age. It's all in God's hands.

My husband and I practice protected sex now. I might have one or two more children and if that happens, I pray that they will also be HIV negative. The chances are good for that result, because I have successfully delivered two children who are negative.

CHAPTER 17

Reconciliation

Tata Coulibaly (pseudonym) is a Malian Muslim woman originally from Ségou. She is twenty-eight years old and is also preliterate. She is one of four children. Ethnically, she is a Bambera.

There are four children in my family and I am the third born. My parents are also from Ségou. I didn't go to school. There was no opportunity for it in my family. When I was old enough, I sold clothes in the marketplace. I am married and have given birth to four children. I had a child before I was married seven years ago, but it is my husband's child. My first born child died. It was a girl who died six years ago. I have since had three more sons. My youngest is one year old.

The first I heard about AIDS was in the marketplace where I work. I heard some older women whispering about someone whom they suspected of having the virus. Several years ago, I started getting night sweats. My husband wanted me to go to Bamako for treatment. I went to a hospital there. I took an HIV test and was told I was seropositive. I stayed with my husband's brother and his family while I was there. I told my brother-in-law about my results. He encouraged me to return to Ségou, because he knew there were clinics here which could treat me just as effectively. That was three years ago.

When I learned more about the ways in which the virus is transmitted, I could only believe that it was a sexual transmission from my husband. I have never been with another man. I know there are other ways of catching this infection, but I was told the most likely way for a woman to get it is from their male partner.

When I learned of my infection, I wasn't afraid at all. The doctors in Bamako immediately assured me that while it would require some lifestyle changes, I would live to be with my children and be their mother. The evidence of that claim is sitting here on my lap. My healthy one year old son is HIV negative.

I was initially very angry with my husband. I refused to let him near me. I had known him for years, given him a daughter prior to our marriage and not been with another man. This is what I got in return for my devotion to him. Only after he begged for my forgiveness and told me he didn't want to lose me and his family that I began to soften. In the end, I still loved him and didn't want to break up our family either.

As it turns out, my husband is also positive, so we are both on treatment. The only person in my family to know about this is my mother. My husband's brother also knows, because he was the one who suggested that we come to Bamako to see the specialist there.

I am thankful for my son, but I don't think I will have any more children. I worried a lot during this pregnancy. It was very tough on me emotionally. I thank God for the successful delivery, but I don't want to go through that again. The doctors told me not to breast feed my son, because there was a chance of the virus passing to him from my milk. I feel bad not breast feeding him like my other children. I hope it won't affect his growth, because a mother's milk is the best. But if it means sparing him from getting this virus, that is the most important thing.

Cursed by Fate

Wasa Sanou (pseudonym) is a Malian Christian woman (a Protestant) originally from Ségou. She is thirty-seven years old and preliterate. She is one of seven children. Ethnically, she is a Bobo. Wasa Sanou was very apprehensive about doing this interview. She had to be assured numerous times that her confidentially would be maintained before she agreed to sit for the interview.

I am the first born child of my parents. My parents had four girls and three boys. Both of my parents are still alive. I never went to school, because I had to stay at home to look after the cows, sheep, and goats. I am married with three children who are fifteen, eleven, and five. I had a fourth child, but she passed away.

I come from a somewhat remote area outside of Ségou. My husband builds houses for a living. We are both Christians. I didn't hear about HIV specifically, but heard many references in church about this affliction that was visited on people who were sexually promiscuous. The preacher said that it was a punishment sent by God to curse this country because of its wickedness. The preacher also said that we had to constantly fight off temptation.

A few years ago, I became sick with a fever and it didn't seem to go away. I consulted several traditional healers who gave me different explanations. The medicine worked for a short time, but the sickness would return. I spent more than a year only doing traditional treatments. I decided that I needed to go to the hospital, because I was starting to have severe diarrhea. The hospital referred me here to the Walé Clinic. It was here that I was tested and received the news that I was HIV positive in 2008.

When I learned of my HIV status, I was very frightened. I believe I started shaking with fear. A worker who was standing nearby thought I was going into a trance as if I was being possessed. It was as if I were staring death in the face. I know I started calling on God spontaneously, asking why this thing was happening to me. I asked if I had done something wrong and this was his punishment from heaven. That is what we heard in the church. I also asked if the ancestors were somehow displeased with some action I had done. I was trembling with fear. I just didn't know what I had done.

After the counselor explained things to me and asked me about my sexual relations with my husband, he suggested that my husband might have had something to do with my exposure. But I didn't believe that because my husband is also a Christian. A Christian cannot marry more than one wife at a time. Besides, why would he do something like this to me? There has to be another explanation for this.

My parents know about the virus and that's it. I have a daughter who is a young woman. I have explained to her that she cannot have many sexual partners and I have told her about using condoms.

My husband and I don't use protection when we have marital relations. The clinic put me on a medication when I became pregnant with my youngest child. They told me the medication would protect the baby from getting the virus in my body. I certainly didn't want him to be cursed with this thing. So far, he is okay. My older daughters were born before I was infected.

Culture of Silence

Safiatou Sylla (pseudonym) is a Malian Muslim woman originally from Niora in the Kayes District. She is forty-six years old and one of ten children. Ethnically, she is a Sarakole.

I am one of ten children. My father has two wives. I am the first born of my mother who is my father's second wife. My husband and I had four children. My oldest, a son, is twenty-five and the youngest daughter will be fifteen.

I completed primary school and then I stopped to help at home. I now sell clothes and make small crafts which I also sell. That's how I support myself and my children. My oldest son also assists with the family as well. I expect him to marry in a few years and to start his own family. That's why I must continue working.

I came to know that HIV can be transmitted through sexual relations, from intravenous drug injection and through blood being contaminated. I learned more by coming to the clinic. My husband died in 2008 of what turned out to be the virus. I have no idea of how he got it, so my assumption is that he got it through a sexual relationship. Very few people in this country inject illegal drugs. I was not aware of any cuts on his body, but honestly, I had never seen him completely naked. He traveled often to bring me clothes that I sold and also brought me the materials that I used for making my crafts. God only knows if he had another family (i.e. another wife). As far as I know, I was his only wife. I don't know. I just don't know.

After he died and was buried, I suspected that I might have something. I had no sickness, but I voluntarily tested at the Walé Clinic in Ségou. I got the news within thirty minutes that I was HIV positive. I thought I was going to die right then and there. My youngest daughter was six years old at the time and I thought I was going to miss out on raising her, because I would be dead.

Once a more thorough analysis of my blood was done, it was another story. My infection had been relatively recent which meant none of my children were seropositive. My CD4 count was high and I was counseled that I wasn't ready to start the medication at that time.

No one in my family knows about my serostatus. That is, none of my sisters or brothers, not even my children or my parents. I am keeping this all to myself. It is my shame to bear. I don't even know anyone else who is positive – not for sure. I have seen other women and men here at the clinic, but no one has said, "I am HIV positive," or "I am seropositive." It is as if we recognize why each other is there, but never say a word or have a discussion about it.

I have since met another man. We have been seeing each other for four years. He does not know about my HIV status. We have never discussed it. He has always used condoms when we have sexual relations. I simply told him that I don't want any more children, so we need to use them.

As I see it, it will be very difficult to start a group like Positive Muslims in Mali. Unenlightened Muslims tend to think that HIV is an illness for those who have engaged in extra marital relations. Such an organization would automatically create stigma. I personally would hesitate to join such a group because I fear the stigma too. We will judge each other in religious matters. Muslims here also think that HIV is a sanction from God. If people came to know that I was seropositive, they might stop buying from me and my livelihood would be threatened. There is not an easy answer in this current state.

I have counseled my older children to be careful in their relationships, and I specifically mean their sexual relationships. I will likely tell the older ones that their father died, because of this virus and that he also gave it to me. I am not cursing his memory, though. I accept what has come, but I am also careful not to expose myself any further. I just want to live and be as healthy as possible. When I see my grandchildren come, I hope to be able to enjoy them.

In Solidarity

Salimata Traore (pseudonym) is a Malian Muslim woman originally from Ségou. She is thirty-six years old and one of three children. Ethnically, she is a Bambera.

We are a family of five. Both of my parents are alive as are my brother and sister. I completed secondary school in Ségou and got married after finishing. It was not an arranged situation.

My husband and I knew each other from school. He was a nice boy from a good background. My family also liked him. When we finished school, he went to my father and asked if we could get married. He paid *la dot* (French for "dowry") to my family and we married in 1997.

I had several miscarriages over the first years of our marriage and I became concerned that I might not be able to carry a child to term. I consulted at least four traditional healers about the situation and each had a different reason for why I could not bring the pregnancy to term. One said it was my own fault and I must have done something wrong. Another one said that after divining the situation (i.e. consulting with the ancestors), he determined that my husband's sperm was not healthy. Finally in 2005, I became pregnant again and was advised to remain off of my feet. The lady doctor who helped me through the pregnancy said some of the previous miscarriages were probably the result of my working too hard while I was pregnant. In any case, God blessed my husband and me with a beautiful baby boy in March 2006. My husband was so proud that I had given him a son, he didn't know how to thank me. His family was also thrilled that I had delivered a male heir for them as well.

I first heard of HIV sometime after my son was born. I am a member of a woman's association called Keneyaton (Bambera for "health association"). Its goal is to promote women's health and wellness issues. The organization assists women in a variety of a ways. If women come from rural areas for health issues, including for HIV consultations, Keneyaton will assist them by providing lodging and make sure they eat while in the area.

The women's organization has also assisted women who have been rejected, or turned out by their husbands and families, because of their HIV status or similar circumstances. We also assist women with their children if they have to work. For women who lose their husband's, Keneyaton also helps women to get financing for micro-projects to develop a skill or start a small scale business.

Keneyaton had a food scheme, but the funds for that program are not sufficient for us to continue it. The goal of the association is to have its own facility. We are hopeful to bring that about. We now have more than 150 members.

It was during one of my health screenings that I found out that I was HIV positive. I started to have certain symptoms which I knew were associated with the virus. My father suggested that I do the test. Back then, a person had to wait at least two weeks to get results. I went back to the clinic where I had gotten tested nearly every day to check on things. They told me each time it would take two weeks. I knew something was wrong otherwise I would have been told something. It was very stressful for me during that waiting period. At the time, there was only treatment in major centers in Mali like Bamako. There was nothing in Ségou. Once I got my seropositive result, I saw only death. I didn't believe the test was right, so I went to another facility to test and that result was also positive. It was an awful month. I was still not convinced, so one of the members from the women's health association suggested that I get tested at Walé. After that test also came back as positive, I accepted the results.

After the diagnosis, there was only treatment for minor infections. Keneyaton was a major help. If it weren't for the support that I received from those brave women, I would have totally collapsed. They encouraged me and told me it was not the end of my life. One or two women revealed that they too were positive. I had no idea of their statuses. Several women told me I was not alone in this crisis.

After receiving encouragement from these very strong women, I decided that I would inform my mother and father about my serostatus. They encouraged me to leave my husband, but I have not taken that advice. I believe it is important for my children to have their father with them. He hasn't been a bad man overall. Apart from this HIV situation, he has been a good provider and a good father to our children. I must try to forgive.

Sometime later, there was a news story about Walé Clinic and someone filmed me without my permission and it was broadcast on national television. My husband has said that it doesn't matter. He said the whole world could know and it wouldn't bother him. It has been a subject which he and I have avoided. He too is positive, but has not discussed the details of how it came about. For now I am content. I have been involved with Keneyaton and believe it or not, I have actually helped myself by assisting other women in their crises. We really do benefit from helping others.

A Fragile Truce

Oumou Diallo (pseudonym) is a Malian Muslim woman originally from Mopti. She is thirty-six years old and one of nine children. Ethnically, she is a Peul.

I am one of several children and was born in Mopti. I attended primary and secondary school in that town. I was married after completing secondary school at eighteen. My first child was born the following year in 1999. I now have four children. My oldest is now seventeen and my youngest is five.

I came to know about HIV in the early 2000s. I was made to understand at the time that it was very contagious.[1] I heard about it through the media such as radio and television, but I first heard it from people talking about it in the town. I remember this woman in a marketplace who spoke with so much authority that I initially thought she was a doctor. I came to learn that she was just acting like she knew more than she did. I remember her saying something about catching the virus if you slept on the same mat as someone with the virus. This is how contagious she said it was. I now know that it can be spread through blood transfusions, from mother to child during the birthing process, from cuts on the skin, and the most often method of transmission is through the exchange of bodily fluids during sexual relationships.

I was contaminated with the virus by my husband, Alieu. He started with a cough that continued and then had flu-like symptoms. He also began having nightmares and would wake up in the morning drenched in sweat. He decided to go to Bamako for treatment. After a week or so, he came back and told me I needed to get an HIV test, because he tested positive. I didn't quite understand what it all

---

1   The human immunodeficiency virus (HIV) is actually not defined as a contagious virus.

meant at the time. I traveled to Ségou with my mother to a clinic to take the test. As we got closer to the town, I became nearly paralyzed with fear. I have a brother who lives in Ségou, so my mother and I stayed with him while we were there. I told him I was going to the clinic, because I seemed not to be able to get pregnant again and was seeking treatment. He didn't know the real reason for my being there.

When I found out I was seropositive, I was furious at my husband for infecting me with this disease. They explained things to me at the clinic. Sexual contact with him was the only way I could have gotten this virus. I cried a lot, because I knew my life would change forever. My mother did not go with me when I was informed of my serostatus. Somehow, I knew bad news was coming and I didn't want her with me when I got it. I was intent on divorcing my husband and when my mother and I returned to Mopti, I went to her house.

The doctor that I saw at the clinic did an analysis of my blood. He told me that even though I tested positive for HIV, my CD4 count was more than 500 and I was told to wait six months and they would check to see if it had gone down. I checked with another doctor in the area and asked if I could start on the ARV treatment because I lived out of the area and I had to travel a great distance. I was allowed to start the treatment. As I said, I went to my mother's house after returning from Ségou. She knew something was very wrong because I had discussed practically everything with her and she knew I was holding on to something. She just kept quiet until I broke down and told her.

When I didn't show up at home as scheduled, my husband, Alieu came looking for me at my family's home. He immediately knew something was wrong when I did not come out to meet him. My mother gave him some vague excuse that I was not feeling well, but she also said that his eyes told her that he didn't believe her. I simply didn't want to see him, or I would have lost my temper with him. I stayed for three days at my mother's without any contact. Finally, my children began wondering why I wouldn't come home, so I had to go and attend to them, but I kept my contact with my husband to a minimum. I greeted him coldly without looking in his direction and said no more. He attempted to speak to me because he was well aware of the source of my anger, but I would not have it.

Apart from Alieu and my mother, no one else knows about my HIV status. Even after I returned home (at the suggestion of my mother), I refused my husband totally because of his giving me this virus. I didn't want him to touch or be near me. He quietly tried to counsel me to be strong. Gradually, I started to listen to him. He told me that even though we had the virus, both of us could continue to live our lives as long as we both took our medication and remained faithful to each other. To this day, however, he has not told me how he was infected, or said who gave the virus to him. I think if I were to confront him about it, I would get mad all over again. We are still together. In fact, it was Alieu who encouraged me to come to meet with you today.[2] He thought it might help me if I spoke to someone about

2   The author, Christopher Brooks.

this situation. I told him that our identities would not be revealed and he said I should do it.

You asked if it is possible for a group of Muslims who are seropositive to form as a cooperative or as a support group. I don't believe such a group is possible. I would not join such a group. It is frankly easier for Muslims in this country to hide their status because many of us fear being judged.

None of my children know about my or their father's HIV status. I would never bring up the topic with any of them. Although my oldest daughter is fifteen years old, I would not discuss such matters with her. I do not plan to inform her of my seropositive status at this point. I am not sure if I ever will. The other children are simply too young, but I won't say anything to them either.

To be honest, I would like to have another child, but I have decided that I will not give my husband another one because of his unfaithfulness. I sometimes still think about divorcing him, but it would involve some public declaration and then the world would know about us having the virus. I would not like to subject our families to that. There is also the matter of our children and protecting them. I would not want them to be subjected to any emotional harm, because of their parents. On those occasions when I have marital relations with my husband, it is protected. If he were to come to me and tell me he wants another wife, I would then divorce him. So far, however, there has been peace in my house, but things could change.

Fear of Exposure

Fatimata Musa (pseudonym) is a Malian Muslim woman originally from Mopti. She is nineteen years old (and was seventeen at the time of the interview) and one of three children. Ethnically, she is a Tuareg. Fatimata was a very nervous informant. Although she was filmed from the neck down like the other key cultural consultants, she feared that someone might recognize her by her clothes. This narrative was very telling in that she represented the experience of many young girls who have been infected by an older man who offers them some financial incentive (such as a motor bike in Fatimata's case) in exchange for a sexual relationship. Oftentimes family poverty might be a driving force in some of these decisions which forces young girls into such situations. It took more than forty minutes to convince her that her identity would be concealed. We traveled to Markala to meet her in the Diamarabugu District.

was born on May 28, 1997 in Markala and am one of three children. I have an older brother and a younger brother. I am the only daughter of my parents. I had a fiancé when I was fifteen, in secondary school but that relationship ended when my future husband found out that I had been involved with a much older man. He became suspicious of my movements and had me followed. I was caught in a situation with the older man. It was this older man who infected me. He bought me a new motor bike when I found out I was seropositive. I told my fiancé to do an HIV test, because he and I had also had sex once. He tested and was negative.

I know one can get HIV through sexual relations, breast feeding, and delivering a baby, and through blood contact. I came to find out this information by visiting a clinic in Ségou. I came to know of my HIV status because I kept getting vaginal infections. I thought it was because I had begun having sexual relations at fifteen years old. When I went to the clinic, I was given an exam. The doctor wanted to do a follow up analysis and also do an HIV test. I then found out that I was infected with the virus in 2013 at sixteen years old.

When I first did the HIV test at the clinic in Ségou, I was told that I was likely to be seropositive. I couldn't quite believe this, so I went to another clinic and my test was negative. I did a third test at the Festival of the Niger River where free testing was being offered. It too indicated that I was negative, so I was convinced that the first test was a mistake. Something in my mind doubted the results of that second and third test because it wasn't handled with the same thoroughness as that first test. I decided to follow up with yet another test. That one confirmed my seropositivity.

When I accepted the reality of my positive status, I immediately became afraid of what my parents would say, especially my father. He has done so much for me as his only daughter. He is an important man and I didn't want to bring him any embarrassment or shame. When my former fiancé broke off our engagement, I asked him if he was going to tell my father the real reason for ending the relationship. He was a real gentleman and told people that I was the one who broke it off, because I wanted to wait until I had completed my studies. He could have humiliated me and told the truth about me, but he did not. I am grateful to him at least for that. My father simply said I was too young to begin with and said nothing more about the matter.

No one in my family knows of my HIV status, and I have kept things quiet. I am fearful that my father will disown me if he finds out that I am seropositive. I have decided that I will have no further sexual relationships. A man proposed marriage to me a short while ago; however, I learned that he was seropositive so I didn't move forward on it.

I have not begun antiretroviral treatments, because my CD4 count remains above 500. The doctor told me that after my count gets below 350, I will begin the treatment.

As for a Muslim-based HIV support group, I think it will be nearly impossible in the current climate of this country. Too many of us think that were we to be involved in an organization like that, our reputations would be ruined. It could affect whether I get married or not. There are many implications involved that could harm my chances. And there is still my father. He might throw me out of the house if he knew how I got this virus. A group like the one you mentioned could hurt us.

As I said, I am abstinent now. I am focusing on my studies. My father has promised to let me go to university if I do well. Somehow, I think he will be more accepting of my situation if I told him I caught this virus as a university student as opposed to being a teenage girl.

Note - *Fatima Musa is now a second year university student.*

A Good Muslim....

Djeneba Katile (pseudonym) is a Malian Muslim woman originally from Sikasso. She is forty-three years old and one of eight children. Ethnically, she is a Samogo.

I am from the Sikasso area and started primary school in that region, so I learned the basics of reading and writing. However, because I am the oldest daughter of my parents, I had to leave school and help raise my younger brothers and sisters. I continued to learn on my own with the help of a family friend. This man had been a teacher at the primary school and sympathized with me and my family situation. He tutored me privately at no cost. I actually came to read and write very well and hope to complete my baccalaureate within the next year. I have been encouraged all of these years by the same teacher who is now elderly. He believes that I should also proceed to the university. One of my younger brothers went to school throughout and eventually completed his university degree. Our entire family is proud of his achievement. He also shared some of his school materials with me and has also been encouraging me to move forward on my educational goals.

* * * * *

I am married and have a daughter who was born in 2006. The marriage was not an arranged one. I have known about HIV/AIDS for a long time. I know it can be contracted through unprotected sexual relations, from mother to child (through the birthing process and also passed through a woman's milk when she is breast-feeding). It can also be contracted when an infected person's blood is introduced to a non-infected person by way of a cut or some other wound. I also know that HIV can be life threatening if not treated. I have also come to know that it was more dangerous in the past when effective treatments were not available in this country.

Now the situation is much better, because there are now several effective treatments for the virus. For those who live in the rural areas it continues to be difficult.

I know all these things because I am one of the early clients to come to the Walé Clinic in Ségou many years ago. I was initially diagnosed in 1996. I was engaged to a man in my early twenties. In order to raise money for our wedding, he traveled to the Ivory Coast to work there. He likely had sexual relations with an infected person, perhaps even a sex worker and contracted the virus. On one of his periodic trips back home, he infected me. Our sexual contact had been unprotected. Since we were to marry, neither of us saw it as a major issue.

When he started getting sick around 1995, there was no effective treatment in this country for the virus. He took many medical tests and his HIV illness was eventually confirmed. Back then, such a diagnosis was essentially a death sentence. He wanted to proceed with the marriage because he said he didn't want to die as a single man. His family also pleaded with me to honor a dying man's final request. I decided, however, I wouldn't go through with the wedding and he subsequently died. I might have reconsidered my decision, but because he never said how he contracted the virus, I was disturbed. His family became embittered with me because I refused to marry their son, but I never told them that I knew of his HIV infection. I am not sure they knew.

I did; however, understand that the chances were good that he had infected me with the virus, so I made arrangements to take the HIV test in Bamako. After giving my blood, I was supposed to know the results in ten to fifteen days. About a week later, however, a social worker from the hospital in Bamako informed me of a new center in Ségou. She thought that might be more convenient for me, since I lived in this area. She said that I would not have to travel such a distance to the capital. That's how I came to know of the Walé Clinic in 1996. At that time there was not an effective treatment for HIV and so I was sure I was going to die. I was afraid because I was only twenty-five years old. I had read that there were effective treatments in Europe. The only problem was that you needed to have a parent of relative who was willing to send the medication to you. I also knew it was very expensive. Since I was a born and bred Malian, I knew I would be left out. I felt desperate and didn't see a way for me to survive.

Once I registered at Walé, I was assured that I could survive this virus because they were receiving new and effective treatment. I received psychological counseling and told not only would I live, but I could get married and have a family. I needed, however, to adhere to my treatment regimen.

I told my parents as well as my brothers and sisters about my virus and also informed them that I was in treatment for it. I also told my father about my now deceased former fiancé and that it was him who had infected me with the virus. I also explained that was the real reason why I did not proceed with the wedding. I told him that I didn't want to marry a man who was about to die. In actual fact I was angry that he had exposed me to the virus. Honoring his dying wish was the least of my interests or concerns. Regardless of his family appealing to me, I refused to go through with it.

My family was very understanding. All of my younger brothers and sisters stood in total solidarity with me. I was still their senior sister and they assured me that the virus would not change my position with them.

Five years after my diagnosis, I met another man and came to love him. After I felt that I had his trust, I decided that I needed to tell him about my seropositivity, but he still wanted to marry me. He was and remains HIV negative. I was thirty years old at the time of our marriage. I was able to give him a lot of information about the virus, but he also received counseling at Walé about practicing protected sex even though my viral load has been undetectable for some time. He was also counseled about under what terms we could conceive a child. In 2005, I became pregnant (after a miscarriage the year before). I gave birth to a beautiful baby girl in 2006. I thought it was a miracle! My daughter was tested over the first eighteen months of her life and was finally declared HIV negative. It was a blessing from God. She will soon turn ten years old.

I am also a member of a support association called Keneyaton, which assists women with health-related issues typically dealing with child care. We also support women seeking temporary lodging and those in need of employment, among other forms of assistance. Although I was embraced by my family after I made them aware of my seropositive status, such has not been the case for many other Malian women. Some have been rejected or disowned by their families after their seropositivity became known. It is a real problem in this country. When someone (man or woman) becomes positive with this virus, it is immediately assumed that they have engaged in some immoral behavior. It is harder for women because in most instances the virus was brought to them by their husbands, fiancés, or boyfriends. That is what happened to me. So mine is not that unusual a scenario. Seropositive women are definitely treated more harshly than men with the virus. They also suffer more severe social costs than men.

As for an HIV positive Muslim support group similar to that in South Africa, I don't think we are ready for that in this country. People still think that those with HIV are not of good character regardless of how they got the virus. According to those who think this way, "A good Muslim cannot be HIV positive." We have to change that kind of thinking if we, as a religious community, will move forward. We also have to change our thinking if we expect our country to make progress in confronting this virus. Using the name "Muslim" in association with such a group would also be problematic. Perhaps something like that can happen in the future, but not now.

I can say that more and more Muslim women are coming to understand that HIV has no economic or social barriers. It can strike anyone. I know mothers whose children contracted the virus from birth. Are those children immoral when they had nothing to do with getting the virus? It was the same when Keneyaton formed. People automatically stigmatized the association, thinking it was full of AIDS-contaminated women. That is only a part of what the association does. Now the organization is well respected. I believe eventually this will be the case in establishing a dedicated Muslim HIV support group in this part of the country. I am confident that it will happen in the future.

My daughter is still young now, but will eventually become an adolescent in a few years. It is then that I will explain to her about how I contracted the virus and how she must not make the same mistakes as I did. She is a sensible young lady and I will do all that I can to protect her. My husband also loves her so much. We both want her to have as fulfilling a life as possible. That means in the face of HIV and AIDS, we must be honest with her about human relationships and what she needs to be aware of. I will also explain that even though I am HIV positive, both she and her father are negative, because I cared enough about both of them to make sure that I took precautions in her very conception. Parents in this country must be willing to speak to their children about such matters, because they are not getting this information in their schools.

CHAPTER 24

Sent by the Ancestors

Sirantou Kone (pseudonym) is a Malian Muslim woman originally from Konna. She is fifty-six years old and one of nine children. She is also pre-literate. Ethnically, she is a Bambera.

I was born in Konna in 1960 and am the sixth born of nine children. However, five of my six brothers have died as well as a sister who has also died. There are only three of us alive now. My sister and I live in the Ségou region, but my brother has remained in Konna. Our parents died there and he wanted to stay in the family homestead. In 2013, the jihadist rebels took control of the town, but he was not harmed in any way. The jihadist, however, wanted to impose strict regulations in those towns that they took control of.

Only one of my brothers went to school and he only completed primary school before stopping. Our parents were very poor and needed us to help on the land that we had. We all worked on it. We had a few animals as well.

I came to live in Ségou when I was about fourteen or fifteen to be married. I was the second of my husband's three wives. There was a younger third wife that he married after me, but she ran off after a short while. We don't know what happened to her, but we never saw her again. My marriage had been arranged by my family. When I moved to Ségou, I was terrified. I had never been away from Konna. My husband's first wife was a very kind woman. She understood that I knew nothing about living in the city and helped me to adjust to my new surroundings. I didn't know anything about being married until she told me what to expect.

I gave my new husband seven children. My first child, a daughter, was born in 1976 when I was fifteen or sixteen years old. My last born daughter is about eighteen. My oldest daughter is a mother with four children of her own. Only two of my seven children are sons.

I came to know that HIV can spread among humans, but animals cannot contract it.[1] I also know that mothers can spread it to their children through their breast milk. Sexual relations is the way that most people in Mali contract the virus.

In the late 1980s my husband became ill. Around the same time, his first wife also began coming down with what we thought was a flu. That wife went to a traditional healer who said that since she and my husband fell ill at the same time they must have been poisoned. I was the obvious suspect. The first wife went to another healer who didn't accuse me, but asked for more precise timing of when my husband became sick and what his symptoms were. He also asked exactly when the first wife became ill. He concluded that they had not been poisoned, but that my husband and his first wife had committed some infraction and the illness had been sent by the ancestors. Their conditions continued to deteriorate and about a year later they died. My husband died in March 2005 and his first wife died at the beginning of August of that year. Since the first wife did not have any children, that added to the conclusion that the second traditional healer had reached. There had to have been some otherworldly offense that caused the first wife to be barren and which also led to their deaths.

By the end of 2005, I started to get ill. When that happened the traditional healer was really persuaded that the ancestors had something to do with what had been happening. It was, however, the very same traditional healer that suggested that I get tested for HIV and I found my way to Walé. That's when my HIV status was confirmed in 2006. My husband must have contracted it and given it to his late wife and to me.

I could only think about my children when I got the news. My children had already lost their father and I was thinking they were about to lose me. None of them is HIV positive, so my husband must have contracted the disease well after our youngest daughter was born.

I started on treatment right away, so my illness must have been advanced. I thought that since my late husband and his first wife were already finished, if I had done nothing I would have followed them to the grave.

My brother and sister know that I am positive. My children also know that I am as well. I think it was important for me to tell them as several of them are married with families of their own. They need to protect themselves and discuss these matters with their children. I knew a woman, Ramata Guindo, who was rejected by her family because she was HIV positive. She died a social death before her physical death. I have had no negative reactions from any of my family, thank God. Ramata Guindo was not so fortunate. She was such a nice woman, but orphaned three children.

---

1   Several species of monkeys, collectively known as simians are susceptible to the virus. It is known as Simian Immunodeficiency Virus or SIV.

* * * * *

Five years ago, I met a man and he wanted us to get married. I agreed. I don't know if he is positive or not, but I have only had protected sexual relations with him and that is it. I am past the age of having children anyway. I am actually his third wife. He typically sees me for one or two nights of the week and then goes to the village where his other wives live. I am living to be a good mother for my children and my ten grandchildren. I want to be here and be a part of their lives.

I am a member of a women's association known as Keneyaton. It was once held under suspicion as an HIV group of loose women. Now the organization is respectable and well known in the Ségou region. I think in time we might be ready for a Muslim HIV support group similar to that in South Africa. But now is not the right time.

Until there is a cure for this virus, we must all protect ourselves. That's why I decided to let my children know about my seropositive status. If my current husband had insisted on having unprotected sex with me, I would have rejected him.

CHAPTER 25

Lost

Oumou Ouattara (pseudonym) is a Malian Muslim woman originally from Koutiala. She gave her age as forty-five, but her appearance suggested that she was closer to seventy, at least. She is pre-literate and is one of five children. Ethnically, she is a Senufo. This was an especially challenging interview and somewhat depressing. Madame Ouattara appeared to be confused on several occasions throughout the interview which suggested perhaps some AIDS-related mental impairment. She seemed remarkably sad throughout the interview which left me questioning if she was sound and if this narrative should be used. This interview was cut short because of a power failure. A subsequent attempt to reach Oumou Ouattara did not yield results.

I am from Koutiala and my ethnic group is Senufo. I am forty-five years old.[1] I get confused very easily, so I am not entirely sure what the correct answer is where my age is concerned. I am one of five children. None of my sisters nor I went to school. My brother went to primary school, but stopped shortly after starting.

My husband died ten years ago and I never remarried. It had been an arranged marriage set up by my parents. He was much older than me, I think. I never knew his actual age. He had taken a second younger wife, but she was not that sociable. When my husband died, the second wife left and went back to her family. I never saw her again. My husband and I had three children. We had two sons and a daughter. I don't know the exact ages of my children. I think my first born is around twenty, but I am not sure.[2]

---

1   This was most certainly not the case. Her appearance suggested someone much older.

2   Given her again and appearance, this information was almost certainly inaccurate.

I don't know much about HIV. I can only tell you that someone brought me to this clinic. I was told to take some pills after I met with someone here. I have suffered a lot of pain. I am in pain right now. I am told that HIV can spread through sexual relations. I also heard something about it on a television program, but I can't remember what was said.

It was here at Walé when I first knew I was HIV positive. After my husband died, I never remarried. A year or so ago I began getting sick with a fever. Someone told me to come back to Walé and that's when I was told I was HIV positive. I believe my husband was also HIV positive and he must have also come here for treatment, but he still died so I don't know if he was helped or not. Only my oldest son knows of my HIV disease. My other children are not aware of this information.

Note - *In 2016 news arrived that Oumou Ouattara had died. It apparently was not from an AIDS-related illness, but she died as a result of a chronic pulmonary infection.*

CHAPTER

26

A Family Blessing

Mariatou Dembele (pseudonym) is a Malian Muslim woman originally from Bla. She is fifty-three years old. She is one of ten children. Ethnically, she is a Minianka.

My name is Mariatou Dembele and I was born in Bla (about an hour's drive from Ségou). I am one of ten children. I have six brothers and three sisters. My parents wanted all of us to be educated. My father was a district administrator and insisted that all of his children go to school. Both my mother and father made all kinds of sacrifices for us to be in school. I made it to secondary school, but stopped when I got married at sixteen. I was in love with this boy named Thierno who was two years older than I. He wasn't that supportive of me continuing with my education and said he wanted a traditional wife, which meant staying home and giving him children. My father was against the idea of my leaving school to get married, but I begged him. I cried so much that he gave in, but not before laying down a condition that I be allowed to continue my education, even if it was informally. Although ours was not an arranged marriage, both families agreed to the terms that my father had specified. He was quite serious and made sure that all parties agreed. I continued to be tutored as my father had made clear.

* * * * *

Over several years I gave birth to five children. I have three sons and two daughters. My oldest son was born in 1979. Thierno was so proud that I had given him a son. His family also loved the idea that I had given birth to a baby boy which continued their family name. My youngest child is also a boy. He was born in 2005. I am proud of all of my children, because every single one of them is educated or in the process of being educated. One of my daughters wanted to stop when she was in secondary school to get married. Her father supported her decision. He said he wanted grandchildren. I said no very firmly. She cried and said I had stopped school and married when I was younger than she was, but I wouldn't hear of it. I didn't respond to her rant. I just kept quiet and looked at her without changing my facial expression. When she calmed down I told her, "If the boy really loves you, he will wait. He will not ask this of you. Your education is the most important thing at this point in your life." She now has an undergraduate degree and is a working mother. She met a very nice young man who was also a university student and married him. On her wedding day, she thanked me for standing firm in my decision not to allow her to get married when she was in secondary school.

* * * * *

As for the topic of HIV, it was certainly an unexpected change in my life. When you find that you have contracted HIV, you are very desperate. It dominates your life and your thoughts. When I came to the Walé Clinic in Ségou, I got more information about the virus. I had read before about how it was transmitted and spread and how a person could protect themselves from infection. I know that it spreads through unprotected sexual relationships. Mothers can also give it to their newborn children and the virus can also be passed on through breast feeding. When a woman is seropositive, she should inform her partner and both parties should use condoms until the virus is suppressed.

In 2005, I began feeling ill. I initially thought it was morning sickness, because I was also pregnant at the time. But there was something different from the morning sicknesses that I had experienced in my past pregnancies. I went in for my routine pre-natal checkup. After a blood test, I was referred to Walé to do an HIV test. I wondered why, of course. In any case, I was tested and received a shock that I was seropositive! I immediately knew it was Thierno who had done this to me. He had been making subtle noises about taking a second wife, but I didn't pay much attention to it.

I called my oldest son and his sister together and told them about my status. I told them I thought that I was finished. I wanted to have a contingency plan in place if I were to have died suddenly. My son and daughter became emotional, because I was crying at the thought of dying. I had thought about suicide, because I didn't want them or any of my children to be stigmatized. I told them that I had gotten the virus from their father. I was so angry with that man I didn't know what to do. I didn't know what was to become of my younger children and my unborn child.

When my sanity returned, I began processing things differently. The psychologist at Walé helped me to regain my composure. The counselor at the clinic said that I needed to begin a medical regimen immediately to protect the unborn baby I was carrying. Of course, I started it right away.

The treatment helped me to deliver a beautiful boy. When he got here, he was perfect. I know mothers aren't supposed to favor one child over the other, but this baby was special because I made changes in my life for him to arrive safely in this world. He is still a wonderful child. His older brothers and sisters dote on him to the point of spoiling him. When I look at the smile on his perfect little face now, I shudder at what I might have done had I not been on that medication. I did not breast feed him when he was born at the advice of the counselor. I felt guilty because I believed that I was somehow depriving him. I know a mother's breast milk is supposed to be the best thing for a child, but I had to give him store-bought milk for his safety.

When I became aware of my seropositivity, I informed Thierno after I told my children. He immediately accused me of being unfaithful, but I knew he was the guilty party and said as much to him. He was about to strike me, but my oldest son was standing nearby and threatened to beat him if he raised his hand to me. Thierno, instead, just left. He eventually went off with another woman, which I suspect was his agenda all along. My thought was, okay he will now contaminate another woman with the virus. He was not around when I gave birth to our youngest child.

A year or so after he abandoned us, Thierno wanted to come back home to reconcile our marriage. He said he was sorry about how he had left and regretted that he wasn't around when our youngest son was born. He said he wanted to be a father to his children and a faithful husband again. I asked him why he had accused me of infecting him with the virus when he knew it was him who had given it to me. I told him I had since read a lot about the Human Immunodeficiency Virus and it was definitely him who had done this. He hung his head low and did not respond to my question. He appeared close to tears. I had my oldest son and daughter present during this entire exchange. He had wanted to speak to me in private, but I refused that request.

At the end of his entreat, I gave him a quiet, but firm no. Under no circumstances would I accept him back again. It had been up to me to endure the shame and humiliation, to calm our crying children who had been teased at school about their "diseased," *sidéenne*[1] mother, and I had not run from any of it as he had run from his family.

Sometime later, one of his brothers came with an imam and tried to persuade me to reconsider my decision and allow him to come back home. I asked my father to be present for that meeting. My father sat very quietly and said nothing throughout the meeting. When the imam and my brother-in-law saw that my position was not likely to change in the slightest, they began appealing to my father. They spoke to him about the Islamic faith and how the "Holy Prophet" (Muhammad) wanted men, women, and their families to be together. They quoted passages from the Quran to support their position. My father never uttered a sound throughout their attempts to appeal to his religious nature. When he spoke, my father calmly said that he had been against my marriage to Thierno from the start. He said he had only given his consent to the wedding after I cried and begged him to let me marry. He said that he was grateful to Thierno because he and I had given him five wonderful grandchildren. But he reminded my brother-in-law and the imam that Thierno had abandoned a pregnant wife (his daughter)

---

1   A pejorative term to refer to someone (a woman in this case) with HIV/AIDS.

who subsequently gave birth to yet another son for him. He said that Thierno had falsely accused his child of something which I had not done which exposed me to public condescension. My father ended by saying that the final decision was mine. He brought me to tears when he said that he was proud of me as his daughter, and that I was more than capable of making such decisions as a grown, responsible woman. My brother-in-law and the imam did not offer a counter argument. They simply nodded their heads in agreement and said no more. They just left. A little later, I saw my brother-in-law and he said that despite the awkward situation between Thierno and me, he, his parents, and the rest of his family still considered me and my children as a part of their family. I subsequently divorced Thierno, but maintain a relationship with his family. They have really embraced me. I refused to request or accept any maintenance from Thierno for our youngest son. I told him he should put it in a bank account to pay for his secondary and university education.

* * * * *

All of my family knows that I am positive. My father is especially proud of me for holding my head high in the face of humiliation. Throughout the ordeal, he repeatedly said that I had done nothing wrong other than to be a faithful and devoted wife. Other people in the community also know that I am seropositive. It is up to them to think what they want to think. I have been avoided by some, but my family and many others have been steadfast supporters. I had to change schools for two of my children, because they were being teased by the other kids. One of my sons wanted to leave school altogether, but I told him I was sorry for what he was experiencing, but he had to continue his education. My daughter told me she was proud that I was her mother and wanted to stay in the same school where she had been teased. I thanked her, but I still moved her. Can you imagine such character from a young girl? My children have been a blessing to me.

I have helped other women who have been disowned by their families because they have the virus. Had it not been for the strength of my parents and the rest of my family, such a path could have been mine. One young lady who was turned away by her family has since become like my child. I kept her in my house for a while. She eventually got married and has recently given birth to a healthy young girl. I consider the baby like one of my grandchildren.

As for an HIV support group for Muslim in this country, it might be a possibility, but there would be challenges that would come with establishing it. We would have to embark on a nation-wide campaign to reduce stigma as an initial step. This is one of the ways that I have benefited from my time at Walé.

I have been very open with my children about my journey with this virus. My youngest son is nearing adolescence and I will tell him about it. I have to say once again that I know I could have had a very negative experience had it not been for the support from my family. I have, in turn, been supportive of those who have been disowned by their love ones. I can only hope that we become more enlightened in this country about HIV, how it spreads, and to avoid the blame that too often comes with it.

I have appeared on television in a public service announcement for the Walé Clinic. I have a job that my father used his connections to help me get, but my goal is to work with doctors to make people aware of this virus. There are many people in African countries who still don't believe HIV is a real disease. There are also many who start the medication, but who subsequently default on their medical treatment. I would love to counsel those people and explain why it is important for them to continue their regimens. I would let them know that I have walked down the same road they are on.

When I have the occasion to counsel infected people, I first find out what is important in their lives (e.g. children, marriage, or it could be their jobs) and tell them that they can have those things, but they have to remain healthy to maintain or reach those goals. The responsibility for achieving those goals, I tell them, rests with them.

I keep male and female condoms at home because several women have come to my house in secret asking for a female condom. Many women have heard about them, but don't know how to use them. Sometimes, my children's friends come to ask me if I have condoms to give them. On occasions, I have to demonstrate to the young men and women how to use them properly. I tell them I am not judging them, I simply want them to be safe.

I remain grateful for some of the experiences that I have had since being infected with this virus. My goal is now to help others have a more positive experience.

CHAPTER 27

Counseled and Counselor

Mahamadou Kouyate (pseudonym) is a Malian Muslim man originally from Mopti. He is fifty-five years old and is one of nine children. Ethnically, he is a Malinke. He is the husband of Djelika Kouyate.

My father had two wives. My mother had four children, but I am the only one of her children who is still alive. My father's other wife had five children. Two of them are dead. Both of my parents are now dead. My mother died a long time ago. My father's second wife died just a few years ago and she lived to be more than one hundred years old.

Of my mother's children, at least one of them, my brother, died of AIDS. He had lived in Abidjan and came back to Mali very ill. In hindsight, he had all the classic symptoms of someone with the virus. He had lost weight and was very wasted when he returned. He also had severe diarrhea, but at the time we didn't know anything. Although he was close to death, he had only hinted at his actual condition. I have since wondered if he actually knew what caused his illness.

I have a contracting business and was trained as a mason. Most of my family has lived in Mopti. I have had three wives and all of them have died. Only one of my wives died of the virus, but I looked after all of them. When I married Fanta, my third wife, and she got sick, that's when I heard about HIV and some of the symptoms. That's when I realized that AIDS must have been the cause of my wife's illness. It also dawned on me that if my wife had AIDS, I must also have it. I decided that we needed to go to the clinic to do the test. I was positive and so was Fanta.

I had not been sexually promiscuous as a youth. I didn't have sex until my first wife and I married in 1987. I was twenty-seven years old. My first and second wives did not display any symptoms of HIV. My first wife had a heart condition and apparently died of it. My second wife was her sister and she too had a heart condition. In addition to that, she also had tuberculosis. There were no autopsies on either of them, so I only went by what I was told. My first and second wives gave me two sons and two daughters each. So I have a total of four children between them.

My third wife went to work in Bamako for some time and I think that's where she contracted the virus. A few years after she came back to this area, she began displaying some of the same symptoms as my brother who had lived in the Ivory Coast and who later died of the AIDS virus. I remembered his illness quite clearly. Just to be sure, I had my sons and daughters tested for the virus. I wanted to know their statuses. Thank God, none of them was positive. My third wife and I had a baby daughter, but she died shortly after she was born. She didn't live to be more than a year old.

It was ten years ago when I learned of my HIV status at the same time of my third wife's diagnosis. When I learned I was infected, I wasn't really surprised. When I was informed of my third wife's seropositivity, I suspected that she had also infected me, and thought it would be the end of my life. I didn't know what would happen to my sons and daughters. They had already lost their mothers. Now, I thought to myself, they are about to lose me. The two oldest children were teens at the time. The youngest was about five years old then. After going to the clinic, I was informed that even though my wife had died of the disease, my infection was relatively recent and it was possible for me to live with the virus after starting treatment.

* * * * *

My son and daughter from my first wife are now twenty-seven and twenty-three. The children from my second wife are now eighteen and fifteen years old. A few years ago, I met Djelika at the clinic. She became my fourth wife. She is also seropositive. She had a horrible incident when she informed her first husband about her positive status. He prevented her from seeing her children and this was a difficult and painful experience for her, although he likely infected her. Together, however, she and I have been very happy, but she spent many years suffering by being denied the opportunity to have a regular relationship with her children.

I have discussed HIV with my three oldest children. They also know of my status. I hope that discussion will be enough to keep them safe. Time will be the ultimate judge.

There is a real stigma surrounding this virus. In the clinic there may be some discussion, but apart from that, you are not likely to hear people talking about it on the streets unless they are whispering to each other or gossiping about someone. Much of that street information is incorrect. I now counsel others that HIV is real. I tell a few of those whom I have counseled and have tested positive that I am living with the virus and so can they. But I also tell others that if they can avoid contracting HIV, they should.

I continue to run my business and have nineteen employees. I asked one of the counselors from the clinic to come and speak to my workers about the virus and how to get completely anonymous testing. Five of them have taken advantage of that offer. One of them has disclosed his seropositive status to me and has begun treatment. I suspect that at least one or two others are also positive, but I won't interfere in their affairs. I have said nothing to them and have no plans to do so. If they need time off from work, I will grant it.

In our society, there are those who think this virus is supernatural, or the result of some sort of sorcery. After burying three wives, I am sure there are those who would accuse me of some kind of sorcery. That is the simplest answer when people just don't know any better, or lack proper information about HIV. Some people just feel they were unlucky and that the virus just chose them. That is an obstacle that we need to overcome in Mali. Educating people about this virus without any moral aspersions attached is the key.

My wife, Djelika, and I use condoms during our marital relations, but not all the time. The clinic said we should continue to use them because we could still infect one another. I am really fortunate to have her. We have been very supportive of each other and her HIV experience has made me more aware of what many HIV positive women in this country are subjected to. We have a lot of work yet to be done.

From Damnation to Acceptance

Seydou Tangara (pseudonym) is a Malian Christian man (a Protestant) originally from Ségou. He is fifty-two years old. He is a preliterate man who is one of several children. Ethnically, he is a Bambera.

My parents had a lot of children, but I don't remember the exact number. There are now three boys and a girl living. I am the second born. Both of my parents are now dead.

I am married with three children. I have three sons whose ages are twenty, eighteen, and the youngest is six. The mother of my two older sons and I are divorced. I remarried nine years ago to a woman named Safiatou and we have a six year old son. My eldest son lives with me and his brother lives with his mother. I primarily work as a bricklayer, but I am also a skilled plumber.

All I knew about HIV/AIDS was that it affected those who had too many sexual relationships. I was also told that if two men had sex, they could also get the virus. I have never had sex with a man and I hadn't had many sexual partners. Frankly, I can't tell you how I got it. There is a chance that my first wife gave it to me, but we never discussed it.

I only had two sexual relationships before I got married, but I had to have contracted the virus after getting married. Had I contracted the virus before marrying, I would have passed it to my older sons and their mother. My oldest son who lives with me was tested and he is HIV negative. I believe my first wife must have contracted it and given it to me somehow. I don't know her status. We divorced, because we didn't get along well. We started disagreeing on practically everything. So, I thought it was better for us to be apart.

I learned of my HIV status in 2008. I was getting sick periodically and I went to a traditional healer. It was the healer who referred me to the clinic to get the HIV test. He had seen several clients with the virus and knew its symptoms. He told me to get the test. He said that if I weren't HIV positive, I should return to him, but if I turned out to be seropositive, the clinic had more effective medicine for the virus than he did.

When I found out I was positive, I thought it was a message of condemnation from God. I didn't quite know what I had done to deserve it. My pastor had told us how God tested Job in the Old Testament and I wondered if I was also being tested in the same way. He had also preached about "AIDS" being a disease of the sinful. He used demeaning terms like sidéen and sidéenne.[1] So I have accepted that I must have done something wrong to get the virus. Apart from my wife and our pastor, no one knows that I am infected.

I have recently begun to volunteer at the clinic. I have seen and learned quite a bit about this virus since volunteering. My pastor suggested that I do something to help others cope with the virus, so I came forward to assist. I had to do some training, but it has been worth it.

Some of the things I have heard people say are startling. When a Muslim woman whom I had been counseling found out I was a Christian, she accused us (i.e. Christians) of spreading the virus to wipe them out. I have counseled young men about having many sexual partners. I also tell them about using condoms as we have been advised at the clinic.

My pastor no longer preaches about the "sin of AIDS." I think he has become more sensitive to how it spreads and that there are many innocent people in our country who had no choice in being infected with this virus. I have also become closer to those who have this virus, especially the women whose husbands or male partners infected and abandoned them.

My oldest son has recently told me he is going to be a father. I insisted that he come to the clinic to get tested. He did, and thankfully is HIV negative. I also suggested that he get circumcised, because it can cut the risk of spreading and contracting the virus significantly. (I also got circumcised and had the procedure done on my youngest son.) He is not sure he wants to marry the woman carrying his unborn child. I have made sure he has plenty of condoms. I may have to tell him about my seropositive status as a last resort. If he is not careful, what happened to me can happen to him.

---

1   A pejorative term for a man or woman with AIDS.

CHAPTER 29

Exiled by Stigma

Aliou Djire (pseudonym) is a Malian Muslim man originally from the Ségou region. He is forty-four years old and is one of four children. Ethnically, he is a Somono.

I am the last born of my parents. They had four children – two boys and two girls and we are all alive. My father died when I was young and my mother died in 2006. I attended school in town and when I wasn't in school, I helped out on my family's farm. My wife and I married in 2001 and we have four children. The oldest was born in 2002, and the youngest in 2014.

I first heard about HIV when I was in my late twenties. A marriage counselor told me about this infectious sickness. Some of my friends were also discussing this "AIDS" (SIDA). I also started hearing about it on the radio and television. Some other things about this virus I heard were so fantastical, I started to believe it was a cover up for something else. Eventually, I stopped believing anything about this virus.

In 2003, I was playing soccer and injured my foot and it became very swollen. I went to see a traditional healer, but it didn't get better. In fact it got worse. It was so painful at one point, I could barely walk on it. After going to another traditional healer, I decided to go to Bamako. I had a brother there who took me to a medical institute for several test. By that time, I had also developed a bad rash on my foot. I suspect that after the first round of tests, the doctors knew something, because they took blood almost immediately. The technician who took my blood did not make eye contact with me after coming back in the room after thirty minutes. The doctor just sent me on to another office. After a second confirmatory test, I was told that I was seropositive.

When I heard those words, "You are seropositive," it was as if time stopped. I didn't know if I was alive or in some kind of suspended animated state. It was terrible, because I thought I was going to die on the spot. I think I must have passed out because I remember when I regained consciousness, my shoes and socks had been removed. I was lying on a sofa in the doctor's office. I didn't remember any of it happening. I told my brother about my diagnosis because he had accompanied me on the medical visit. I also started the treatment regimen. I let my wife know about my seropositivity and told her she also needed to test. She also turned out to be seropositive.

I'm not sure how they found out, but some people in the village came to know that my wife and I were seropositive. We were mocked and ridiculed for having weak morals. I had lost a little weight and I think that must have given some of the villagers the idea that I was infected. I have no idea how else this could have become known. We do know that it was the negative reaction to our seropositive status that caused us to leave the village and move to Ségou. Neither of us has been back to the village in a few years.

Although my wife and I are seropositive, none of our children is. Our oldest daughter is thirteen (soon to be fourteen) and she was born before our diagnosis. The other children ages eight, seven, and one were born after the diagnosis. My wife was on treatment to prevent her from spreading the virus to them.

My oldest daughter has begun to show signs of womanhood. My wife will speak to her about the changes in her body, and I want to tell her not to have many sexual relationships. My sons are too young to have such a discussion. I have advised many of my friends that if they anticipate a sexual relationship, they should use a condom.

My sexual relations with my wife are protected. The only time we don't use protection is when we are trying to have a child and we get counseling before doing that. We don't plan to have any more, but she might change her mind.

I hope there will be a vaccine for this virus soon. I am not so worried about myself, but I don't want my children to live their lives under this shadow. This virus has been with us since I was a child. It has really hurt us in Africa. I pray that I will live to see the day when AIDS is no more.

Bibliography

Bwayo J, Plummer F, Omari M, et. al. "Human immunodeficiency virus infection in long distance truck drivers in east Africa." *Archives of Internal Medicine*, June 27, 154 (12) 1994: 1391 – 1396.

Benton, Adia. *HIV Exceptionalism: Development through Disease in Sierra Leone.* Minneapolis: University of Minnesota Press, 2015.

Brooks, Christopher A. *Through the Voices of Men: South African Men Speak about HIV.* Linus Publications, June 2011. Second revised and expanded edition, July 2013.

Boileau, Catherine, B. Vissandjee, V. K. Nguyen, S. Rashed, M. Sylla, and V. Zunzunegui. "Gender Dynamics and Sexual Norms among Youth in Mali in the Context of HIV/AIDS Prevention." *African Journal of Reproductive Health / La Revue Africaine De La Santé Reproductive* 12.3 (2008): 173-84.

Carillon, Séverine. «Les Ruptures De Suivi Médical Des Personnes Vivant Avec Le VIH á Kayes (Mali). Approche Anthropologique. " *Sciences Sociales Et Santé.* 29 (2) 2011 : 5. Web.

Diallo S, Toloba Y, Coulibaly SA, Dabitao D, Diop S, Doumbia S, Keita B. "Male circumcision and HIV in the Malian military." *Le Mali Médical.* 23 (1) 2008: 45-6.

Do, Natalie., Kelesitse Phiri, Herman Bussmann, Tendani Gaolathe, Richard G. Marlink, and C. William Wester. "Psychosocial Factors Affecting Medication Adherence Among HIV-1 Infected Adults Receiving Combination Antiretroviral Therapy (cART) in Botswana." *AIDS Research and Human Retroviruses* 26 (6) 2010: 685 – 691.

Essa, Azad. "HIV/AIDS and Africa's military: Are we winning this war?" *Pambuza News*, December 2008.

Fleshman, Michael, "AIDS prevention in the ranks UN targets peacekeepers, combatants in war against the disease." *Africa Recovery*, June 2001.

Gray, Peter B. "HIV and Islam: Is HIV Prevalence Lower among Muslims?" *Social Science and Medicine*, 58 (4) 2004: 1751 -1756.

Hasnain, Memoona. "Cultural Approach to HIV/AIDS Harm Reduction in Muslim Countries." *Harm Reduction Journal.* BioMed Central, 2005.

Henry, Emilie, A. Bernier, F. Lazar, G. Matamba, M. Loukid, C. Bonifaz, S. Diop, J. Otis, and M. Préau. "Was It a Mistake to Tell Others That You Are Infected with HIV?": Factors Associated with Regret Following HIV Disclosure Among People Living with HIV in Five Countries (Mali,

Morocco, Democratic Republic of the Congo, Ecuador and Romania). Results from a Community-Based Research." *AIDS and Behavior*, (19) 2015: 311 - 321.

Hess, Rosanna F., and Martin Mbavu. "HIV/AIDS Fatalism, Beliefs and Prevention Indicators in Gabon: comparisons between Gabonese and Malians." *African Journal of AIDS Research*, 9 (2) 2010: 125 - 133.

Hess, Rosanna F., and Dawn McKinney. "Fatalism and HIV/AIDS Beliefs in Rural Mali, West Africa." *Journal of Nursing Scholarship* 39 (2007): 113-18.

"In Mali, HIV/AIDS Remains Shrouded in Silence." UNICEF, 13 March, 2014.

Loue, Sana. "AIDS Jihad: Integrating the Islamic Concept of Jihad with HIV Prevention Theory." *Journal of Health Care for the Poor and Undeserved* 22 (3), 2011: 720 – 739.

Lynch, Ingrid et. al.,, "Constructed of masculinity among a group of South African men living with HIV/AID: reflections on resistance and change." *Culture, Health & Sexuality* Vol. 12, No. 1 January 2010: 15 – 27.

Mali, *Enquête par grappes à Indicateurs Multiples (MICS) 2015 Rapport de Résultats Clés*, March 2016.

Mills, Greg. "AIDS and the South African Military: Timeworn Cliché or Time bomb?" *HIV/AIDS: a Threat to the African Renaissance?* Occasional paper (Johannesburg, South Africa: Konrad Adenauer Foundation, 2000.

Mulanga-Kabeya, C., E. Morel, D. Patrel, E. Delaporte, F. Bougoudogo, Y. I. Maiga, Z. Diawara, I. Ndoye, S. Garangue, and D. Henzel. "Prevalence and Risk Assessment for Sexually Transmitted Infections in Pregnant Women and Female Sex Workers in Mali: Is Syndromic Approach Suitable for Screening?" *Sexually Transmitted Infections*, 75, October 1999: 358 - 360.

Kippenberg, Julianne. "Dispatches: Gold Refiners Should Act on Child Labor" *Human Rights Watch*, June 12, 2015.

Niang, Cheikj I., P. Tapsoba, E. Weiss, M. Diagne, Y. Niang, A. Moreau, D. Gomis, A. Wade, K. Seck, and C. Castle. "'It's Raining Stones': Stigma, Violence and HIV Vulnerability among Men Who Have Sex with Men in Dakar, Senegal." *Culture, Health & Sexuality*, volume 5 (6) 2003: 499 - 512.

Obermeyer, Carla Makhlouf, and Michelle Osborn. "The Utilization of Testing and Counseling for HIV: A Review of the Social and Behavioral Evidence." *American Journal of Public Health*, volume 97 (10) 2007: 1762 - 1774.

Office du Niger Ségou. *Plan de Lutte Contre Le VIH/SIDA en Zone Office du Niger*. No date.

Oumar Baa, Christopher O'Reganb, et. al., "HIV/AIDS in African militaries: an ecological analysis." *Medicine, Conflict and Survival*, volume 24, No. 2, April – June 2008: 88 – 100.

Pagezy, Helen, and Le Palec, Annie. "Vivre avec le VIH au Mali. Stratégies de survie,» Paris, L'Harmattan, 271 (2003).

Présidence de la République, *Recueil des textes sur la lutte contre le VIH/sida*. Bamako : Haut Consiel National de Lutte Contre le Sida, 2006.

Rafiq, Muhamed Yunus. "The HIV/AIDS Epidemic in Muslim Africa: Tanzania as a Case Study." Institute for Social Policy and Understanding, Policy Brief, Dec. 2009.

Speakman, Sloane. "Comparing the Impact of Religious Discourse on HIV/AIDS in Islam and Christianity in Africa." Vanderbilt Undergraduate Research Journal 8 (2012): 1 – 7.

Steuer, Noemi. "'We are just afraid of what others may say about us.' Maintaining honor and respect in processes of disclosure in Bamako, Mali." Medische Anthropologie 24 (2) 2012: 266 – 287.

Trinitapoli, Jenny, and Mark D. Regnerus. "Religion and HIV Risk Behaviors among Married Men: Initial Results from a Study in Rural Sub-Saharan Africa." *Journal for the Scientific Study of Religion* 45 (4) December 2006: 505-28.

UNAIDS. *Collaboration with traditional healers in HIV/AIDS prevention and care in sub-Saharan Africa A literature review*. Geneva, Switzerland: UNAIDS, 2000.

UNAIDS. *Global Report*. Geneva, Switzerland: UNAIDS, 2010.

UN Security Council Resolution 1308 on the Responsibility of the Security Council in the Maintenance of International Peace and Security: HIV/AIDS and International Peace-keeping Operations. July 2000.

Wadud, Amina. *The Qur'an and Woman: Rereading the Sacred Text from a Woman's Perspective*. New York: Oxford University Press, 1999.

Wadud, Amina. *The Gender Jihad: Women's Reform in Islam*. Oxford: One World Press, 2006.

Winskell, Kate, Elizabeth Hill, and Oby Obyerodhyambo. "Comparing HIV-related Symbolic Stigma in Six African Countries: Social Representations in Young People's Narratives." *Social Science and Medicine* (1982). 73 (8) October 2011: 1257 -1265.

World Bank prevalence of HIV totals (ages 15 – 49) http://data.worldbank.org/indicator/SH.DYN.AIDS.ZS.

Yamaguchi, Kaoru. *HIV/AIDS in the Muslim-Majority Countries: Formula for Low Prevalence*. Bemidji State University, 2012:1 - 54.

Zou, James, Yvonne Yamanaka, John Muze, Melissa Watt, Jan Ostermann, and Nathan Thielman. "Religion and HIV in Tanzania: Influence of Religious Beliefs on HIV Stigma, Disclosure, and Treatment Attitudes." *BMC Public Health*, (9) 75 March 2009.